To
Happy
From Your Twin
Love
Fran

LAND OF BLACK VOLCANOES AND WHITE SANDS

The Pinacate and Gran Desierto de Altar Biosphere Reserve

Larry G. Marshall
Clark Blake

Dedicated to James T. Gutmann, Friend and Scholar

and

In Commemoration of the Centennial of the Hornaday Expedition

JAMES T. GUTMANN AT RED CONE CAMPGROUND 2007. Peggy Gutmann

CONTENTS

PREFACE

For thousands of years, the native peoples in the Pinacate area of the northwestern Sonoran Desert lived harmoniously with their natural environment. They used only what was necessary to supply their food, shelter, and tribal space. In the mid-sixteenth century, invading peoples arrived from the Old World. They introduced horses, goats, cows, and—intentionally or by accident—a wide variety of exotic plants and diseases. The Sonoran landscape and its people faced new challenges and irreversible change.

Centuries passed before people recognized the need to protect the Pinacate region's biological, geological, archaeological, and historical resources, but, finally, in July 1993, the Mexican government decreed "The Pinacate and Gran Desierto de Altar Biosphere Reserve"—a natural protected area of more than 2,700 square miles (7,146 km^2). This decree enabled restoration and revitalization of its degraded natural environments, and provided members of the local community, visitors, and researchers with a place to experience its scenic wonders and biological diversity, now protected for generations to come.

The Pinacate reserve is contiguous with Organ Pipe Cactus National Monument and Cabeza Prieta National Wildlife Refuge to the north, both in southwestern Arizona. To the west it borders the Upper Gulf of California and Colorado River Delta Biosphere Reserve located in the northernmost part of Mexico's fabulous Sea of Cortez.

The creation of these biosphere reserves has proved strategic, not only for the obvious protection of their natural elements, but also for the opportunities they afford in the exchange of experiences, observations, and skills between natural resource managers in the United States and Mexico—contributing to more effective international conservation. In 2008, we can say that conservation of natural resources is no longer a "trend," but a firm reality. Conservation practices today recognize and acknowledge the importance of increased sustainable development of human communities, the environment, and the natural resources in special places.

Conscious that *we protect what we know*, the authors of this book describe the geology, plants, animals, and human history of this special place. Travelers passing through the area and visitors to the reserve will be able to use this book to observe, get acquainted with, and understand the land's natural and historical happenings from prehistoric past to present. Written with the help of experts and enthusiasts in each of the topics covered, the book also serves as a valuable reference.

Welcome to giant sand dunes, steep and massive volcanic mountains and craters, and an inimitable mix of native plants and animals! Hopefully, the Pinacate will serve this and future generations as an inspiration and an example of how to respect and humbly protect Earth's landscapes and life forms.

Por miles de años, los grupos nativos en el área del Pinacate, en el noroeste del desierto Sonorense, vivían armoniosamente con el medio natural que los rodeaba. Utilizaban sólo lo necesario para cubrir sus necesidades de alimento, refugio y espacio tribal. A mediados del siglo XVI, personas invasoras llegaron del Viejo Mundo. Ellos introdujeron caballos, chivas y vacas y, consciente o inconscientemente, una gran variedad de plantas exóticas y enfermedades. El paisaje del desierto Sonorense y su gente se enfrentaron a nuevos desafíos y fueron empujados hacia cambios irreversibles.

Los siglos pasaron y gradualmente la gente se fue dando cuenta de la necesidad de proteger los recursos biológicos, arqueológicos, geológicos, e históricos de esta área. Finalmente, en Julio de 1993 el Gobierno Mexicano decretó la Reserva de la Biosfera Pinacate y Gran Desierto de Altar un área natural protegida de mas de 7000 km^2. Esta decisión permitió la restauración y revitalización de ambientes naturales degradados. También proveyó a miembros de la comunidad, visitantes e investigadores, de un lugar en donde experimentar los valores escénicos y la diversidad biológica.

La región del Pinacate se encuentra contigua al Monumento Nacional de Organ Pipe Cactus, así como el Refugio de Vida Silvestre de Cabeza Prieta, ambas en la parte suroeste del estado de Arizona. Al oeste colinda con la Reserva de la Biosfera Alto Golfo de California y Delta del Río Colorado en la parte más alta del fabuloso Mar de Cortés.

Las reservas de la biosfera representan una oportunidad estratégica de conservación internacional. Han influenciado el intercambio de experiencias de manejo de recursos naturales entre el personal de las áreas protegidas de ambos países. La conservación de recursos naturales no es una 'moda', sino una realidad. Identifica y reconoce la creciente importancia del desarrollo sostenible de comunidades humanas, el medio ambiente, y los recursos naturales en lugares especiales.

Conscientes de que *se protege lo que se conoce*, este libro describe la geología, flora y fauna, e historia humana de este lugar especial. Al viajar por la región, los visitantes podrán observar, conocer y entender los fenómenos naturales e históricos del pasado y el presente. Escrita con la ayuda de expertos y entusiastas en cada uno de los tópicos cubiertos, esta libro es también una valiosa herramienta de consulta.

Les damos la bienvenida a las grandes dunas de arena, la escarpada serranía volcánica y la mezcla única de plantas y animales nativos. Esperemos que el Pinacate sirva a esta y futuras generaciones de inspiración y ejemplo para lograr el respeto y la protección de la vida y los paisajes en el planeta Tierra.

Federico Godínez y José Dávila Paulin
Director y Subdirector
Reserva de la Biósfera El Pinacate y Gran Desierto de Altar

INTRODUCTION

The Pinacate, for many, is the heart and soul of the Sonoran Desert.[1] The magic and wonder of this landscape lies in its dynamic and violent geologic history,[2] which has left a vast, desolate expanse contrasting a black, "moon-scape" volcanic field and a stark-white sea of sand dunes. It is a land layered with ancient ash, lava, and parched desert sands[3] that stretch to meet the shallow salt waters of the Gulf of California and Colorado River Delta. Majestic and secluded, the landscape inspires awe and reflection in all who visit.

While many see it as exquisite, explorers and natural historians have variously described the landscape as alien, dangerous, isolated, mysterious, peculiar, silent, strange, and unfriendly. For visitors, it is a common, haunting experience to hear no extraneous sounds and see no other human beings. This place has long been a sacred land for native peoples; the Hia C'ed O'odham believe it is the place of their creation.

THE PINACATE, FOR MANY, IS THE HEART AND SOUL OF THE SONORAN DESERT.

The reserve is located in one of the hottest, driest, and most desolate parts of the Sonoran Desert, where the climate indiscriminately challenges plants, animals, and humans. Despite the dearth of rainfall and extreme summer temperatures, the area supports a remarkable desert-adapted diversity of life. The flora and fauna include at least 506 species of vascular plants, thousands of species of invertebrates, 2 species of closely related native freshwater fishes, 4 species of native amphibians, 44 species of native reptiles, 237 species of resident and migratory birds, and 38 species of native mammals.

The region also contains a rich and diverse archaeological record going back many thousands of years,[4] much of which remains unaltered by erosion. The youngest volcanic rocks geologists have dated here are about 12,000 years old, give or take 4,000 years.[5] Other, undated, eruptions may be younger. The northern edge of the volcanic field includes a segment of the infamous "Devil's Highway," a fiercely dry and dangerous trail taken by early native peoples and, later, intrepid travelers of many nations.

The overlap of human occupation in the American Southwest—dating to many thousands of years ago—and volcanism in the Pinacate encourages us to wonder. Did early humans witness scorching lava flows and showers of hot ash? Did the Earth literally tremble under their feet to inspire myths of creation and doom? How did this barren, stark

THE MAGIC AND WONDER OF THE PINACATE LIES IN ITS DYNAMIC AND VIOLENT GEOLOGIC HISTORY.

PINACATE MEANS STINK-BEETLE. IT DERIVES FROM *PINACATL* OF THE *NAHUATL* LANGUAGE OF THE AZTECS. THIS IS A LARGE, BLACK BEETLE (*ELEODES ARMATA*), WHICH STICKS ITS HIND-END UP VERTICALLY TO EMIT A FOUL ODOR WHEN THREATENED.[6] THE O'ODHAM CALL IT BITOKOI.[7]

PINACATE BEETLE Francis M. Harty

landscape impact the first European explorers and travelers? Undoubtedly, prehistoric inhabitants and newcomers from the Old World contemplated this striking landscape. Certainly, they left their mark on it.*

But the story of the Pinacate is not all about the past, and neither is the wonder. Today's visitors still ask themselves, "how," "when," "where," and "why"? Some answers can be found in science, some in the legends and lore molded by the landscape, and still others in each individual's experiences and perceptions as they explore this enchanting land.

*Because of the reserve's recent history and location, many place names or terms in this guide are translated into Spanish. Terms from Native American or Old World languages are specifically identified.

In the 1960s and '70s, the moon-like terrain served as a training ground for Apollo astronauts prior to lunar missions. This is one of the few places on Earth that provides an "extraterrestrial" landscape and experience. The lava field is so vast and distinct in appearance that it is easily identified in satellite images and in photos taken by astronauts on space-shuttle missions.

THE BIOSPHERE

The Pinacate and Gran Desierto de Altar reserve is located in the far-northwest corner of the state of Sonora, Mexico. It comprises an area of about 2,760 square miles (7,146 km^2) or 1,962,553 acres (794,245 ha). Some 770 square miles (2,000 km^2) are volcanic landscape with lava flows, cinder cones, and one of the world's largest concentrations of giant "maar" craters. It also contains some 1,930 square miles (5,000 km^2) of sand dunes lying between the volcanic field and the Gulf of California.

The first official attempt to protect the Pinacate area came in the mid-1970s, when the Mexican Government decreed 100 square miles (260 km^2) as a Wildlife Refuge and Forest Reserve.[8] During the early 1980s, an ecological survey was conducted that highlighted the unique combination of natural elements. Based on public interest on both sides of the border, in 1993 the internationally recognized reserve was established to conserve the area's natural biodiversity and to promote its sustainable use.[9]

The establishment of the reserve was promulgated and approved by the government's *Secretaría de Medio Ambiente, Recursos Naturales y Pesca* (SEMARNAP). SEMARNAP committees advising on historical-cultural, scientific, ecotourism, and security issues helped develop a management plan that recognizes the need to collaborate with the native O'odham people for continued traditional access and use of resources.[10]

BIOSPHERE RESERVE SIGN. Photo courtesy Organ Pipe Cactus National Monument

RESERVE

PINACATE, GRAN DESIERTO AND UPPER GULF OF CALIFORNIA.
Thematic Mapper Satellite Imagery, U.S. Geological Survey Open-File Report 00-309, 2001

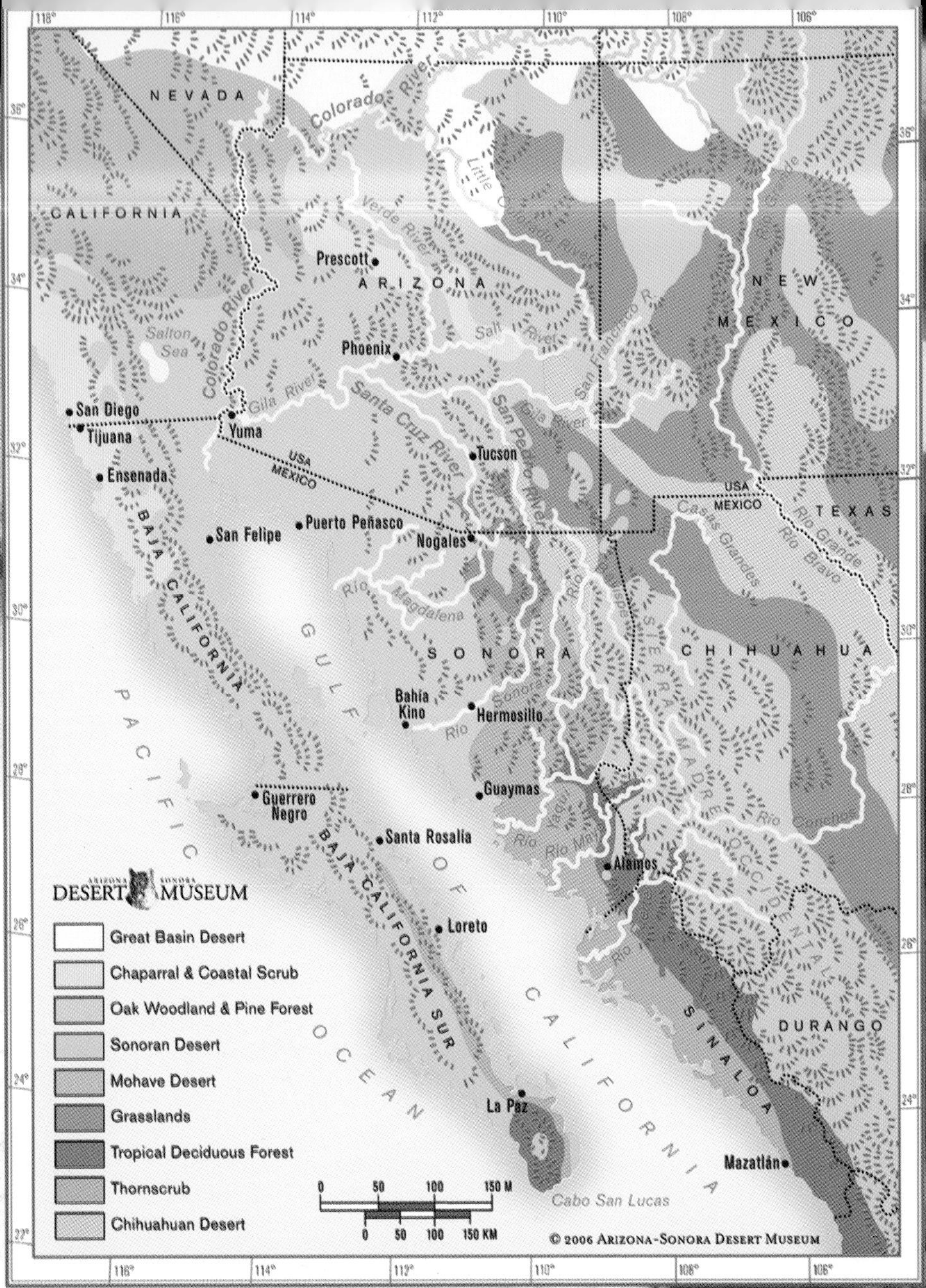

SONORAN DESERT. Arizona-Sonora Desert Museum

PINACATE FROM SPACE SHUTTLE. LOOKING NORTH (LEFT PHOTO) AND SOUTH (RIGHT PHOTO) ALONG GULF OF CALIFORNIA. Images (ISS002-E-6416) (STS040-073-054)
Image Science & Analysis Laboratory, NASA Johnson Space Center

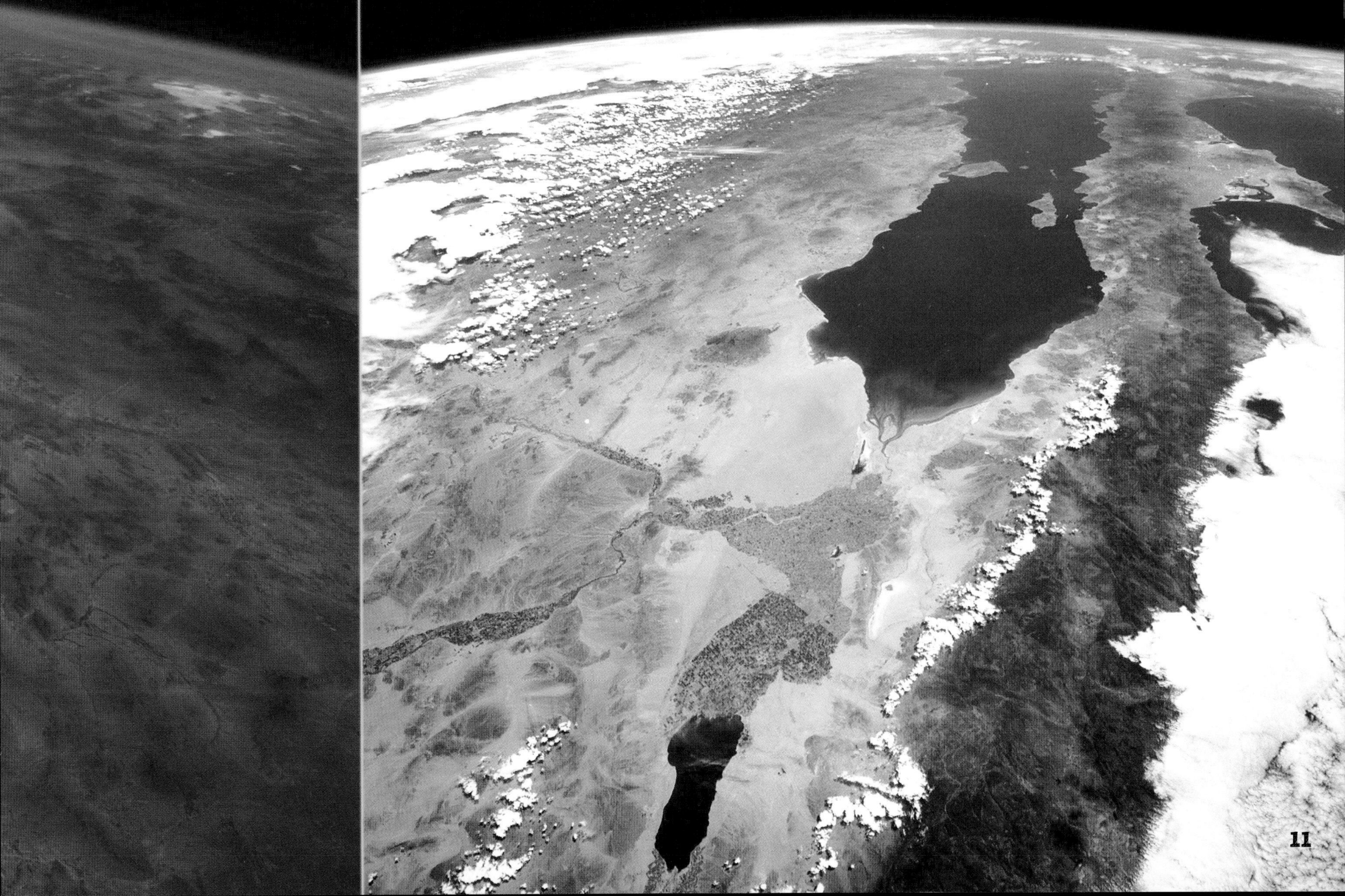

THE NAME "SONORA" DERIVES FROM AN AREA, A RIVER, AND A VALLEY THAT WAS CALLED *SENORA* BY OPATA NATIVES IN THE 1540S. THIS NAME WAS TRANSMUTED INTO "SEÑORA" BY EARLY SPANIARDS AND LATER TO "SONORA." [11]

The Sonoran Desert is among the most biologically diverse deserts in the world. It covers about 100,000 square miles (259,000 km^2) and surrounds much of the Gulf of California. Its rainfall and temperatures vary considerably across its expanse. The Pinacate is located in its hottest and driest portion, the Lower Colorado Valley subdivision of the Sonoran Desert. The reserve lies within the Sonoran Warm Desert scrub vegetation type as defined by botanists, and the Sonoran Biotic Province as defined by biogeographers and zoologists. [12]

For management purposes, the reserve is divided into two core zones and a buffer zone. The core zones are more heavily regulated, with strict

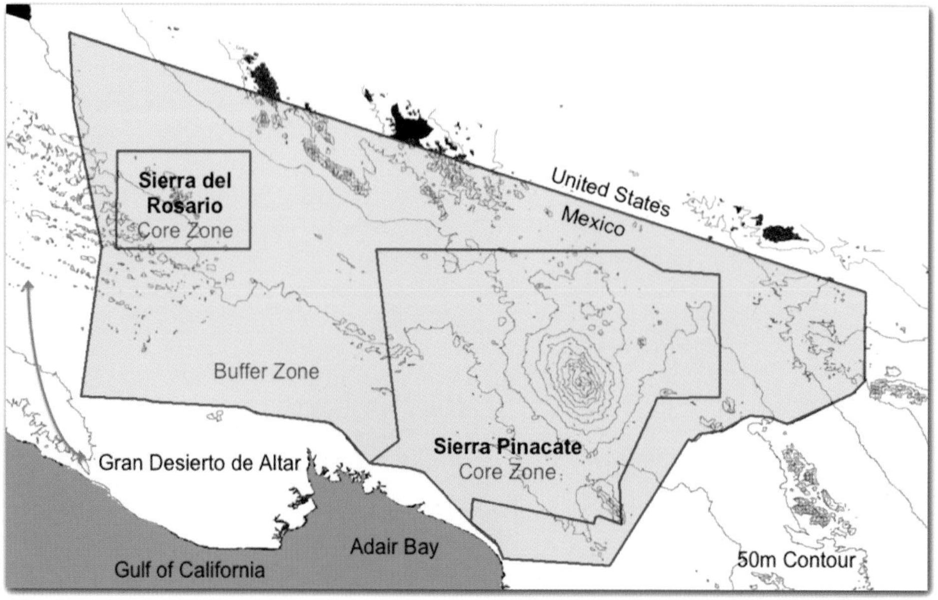

TOPOGRAPHIC MAP OF PINACATE BIOSPHERE RESERVE SHOWING CORE AND BUFFER ZONES. José Dávila Paulin

SIERRA DEL ROSARIO

© Arizona-Sonora Desert Museum. Mark Dimmitt

Photo by Peter L. Kresan

BIOSPHERE RESERVES are promoted and designated by the United Nations Economic, Scientific and Cultural Organization's "Man and the Biosphere" Program. They are made up of terrestrial and/or coastal ecosystems where maintenance of biodiversity and sustainable human use is encouraged. Biosphere reserves are internationally recognized. They are nominated and designated by sovereign national governments, and remain under the jurisdiction of those countries. The reserves serve as living laboratories for demonstrating the integrated management of land, water, biodiversity, and human enterprise. Biosphere reserves strive to fulfill three complementary functions: (a) conservation of landscapes, ecosystems, species, and genetic variation; (b) socio-cultural and ecological sustainable development; and (c) logistical support for research, education, and information exchange related to conservation issues.[13]

guidelines for visitors. They consist of two discontinuous areas: the Sierra del Rosario, covering an area of about 160 square miles (414 km^2), and the Sierra Pinacate, with an area of about 880 square miles (2,281 km^2). The less-regulated buffer zone of some 1,720 square miles (4,450 km^2) surrounds the two core zones. (The Sierra Pinacate has also been called Sierra El Pinacate, Sierra de El Pinacate, and Sierra del Pinacate.)

The Pinacate reserve is among a cluster of recently protected areas along the U.S.-Mexico border, which collectively comprise 9,266 square miles (24,000 km^2) of Sonoran Desert. In Mexico, the Upper Gulf of California and Colorado River Delta Biosphere Reserve (*Reserva de la Biósfera del Alto Golfo de California y Delta del Río Colorado*) lies to the west and southwest. In the United States, the Cabeza Prieta National Wildlife Refuge and the contiguous Barry M. Goldwater Range lie to the north of the reserve, and the Sonoran Desert National Monument and the Organ Pipe Cactus National Monument lie to the northeast.

The Pinacate and Gran Desierto de Altar Biosphere Reserve and the Organ Pipe Cactus National Monument are "sister" biosphere reserves, with management teams that collaborate on long-term monitoring programs and collectively seek solutions for common challenges and needs.

GEOGRAPHIC SETTING

Pinacate

The Pinacate is a volcanic field about 25 miles (40 km) east-to-west and 40 miles (65 km) north-to-south. Its northern edge, called the "Pinacate lava flows," extends into the southern part of the United States at the Cabeza Prieta National Wildlife Refuge. The lava field is so vast and distinct in appearance that it is easily identified in satellite images and in hand-held camera photos taken by astronauts on space-shuttle missions. The volcanic rocks form a shield volcano whose lavas range in

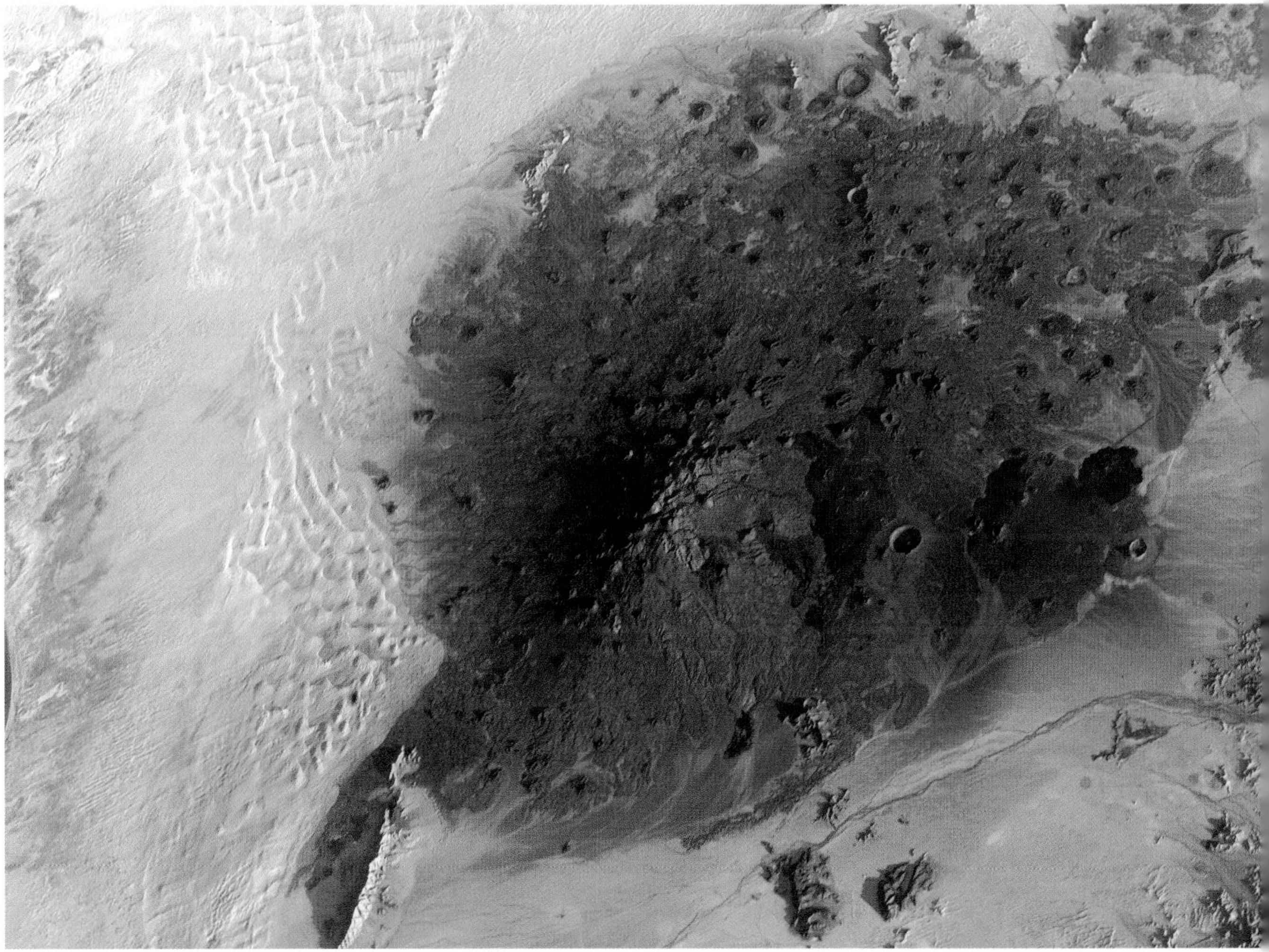

SPACE SHUTTLE PHOTO OF PINACATE VOLCANIC FIELD. Image (ISS004-E-12326) Image Science & Analysis Laboratory, NASA Johnson Space Center

age from more than 1.7 million years to 1.1 million years and are overlain and flanked by younger cinder cones, lava flows, and craters.[14] Geologists estimate that 58 to 70 cubic miles (242 to 270 km^3) of lava erupted in this field over the last few million years.[15]

Sometime prior to 1.7 million years ago, basalt flows erupted in the Pinacate region, their hot, fluid sheets extending significant distances from the source of their eruption. This shield volcano forms the Sierra Pinacate, a mountain range (*sierra* in Spanish) variously referred to as Volcán El

Pinacate, Sierra de Santa Clara, and Volcán Santa Clara on some Mexican maps.[16] Native O'odham call it *Schuk Toak* (which translates to black mountain but refers to the range). The coordinates of its central peak are 31° 46' 20" north latitude, 113° 29' 54" west longitude. At 3,957 feet (1,206 m) above sea level, Santa Clara Peak (also known as Pinacate Peak) is the highest point in the Pinacate. Carnegie Peak, just east of Santa Clara Peak, is the second highest peak at 3,708 feet (1,130 m) above sea level.[17]

PINACATE VOLCANIC FIELD FROM GRAN DESIERTO. Bill Glass

PROTECTED AREAS SURROUNDING PINACATE BIOSPHERE RESERVE ALONG U.S.-MEXICO BORDER.
Ami Pate

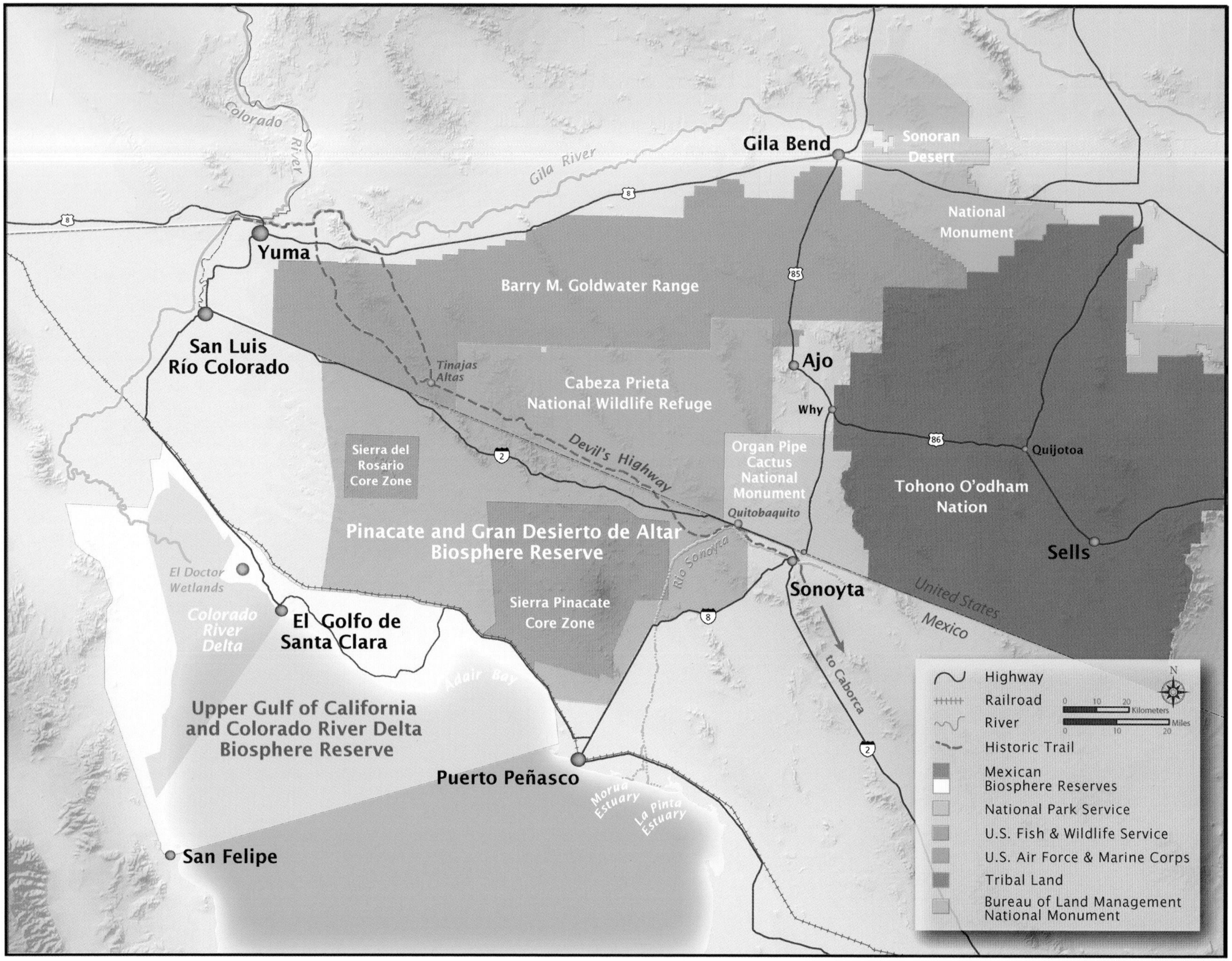

SATELLITE IMAGE OF PINACATE VOLCANIC FIELD AND LANDSCAPE FEATURES. Ami Pate

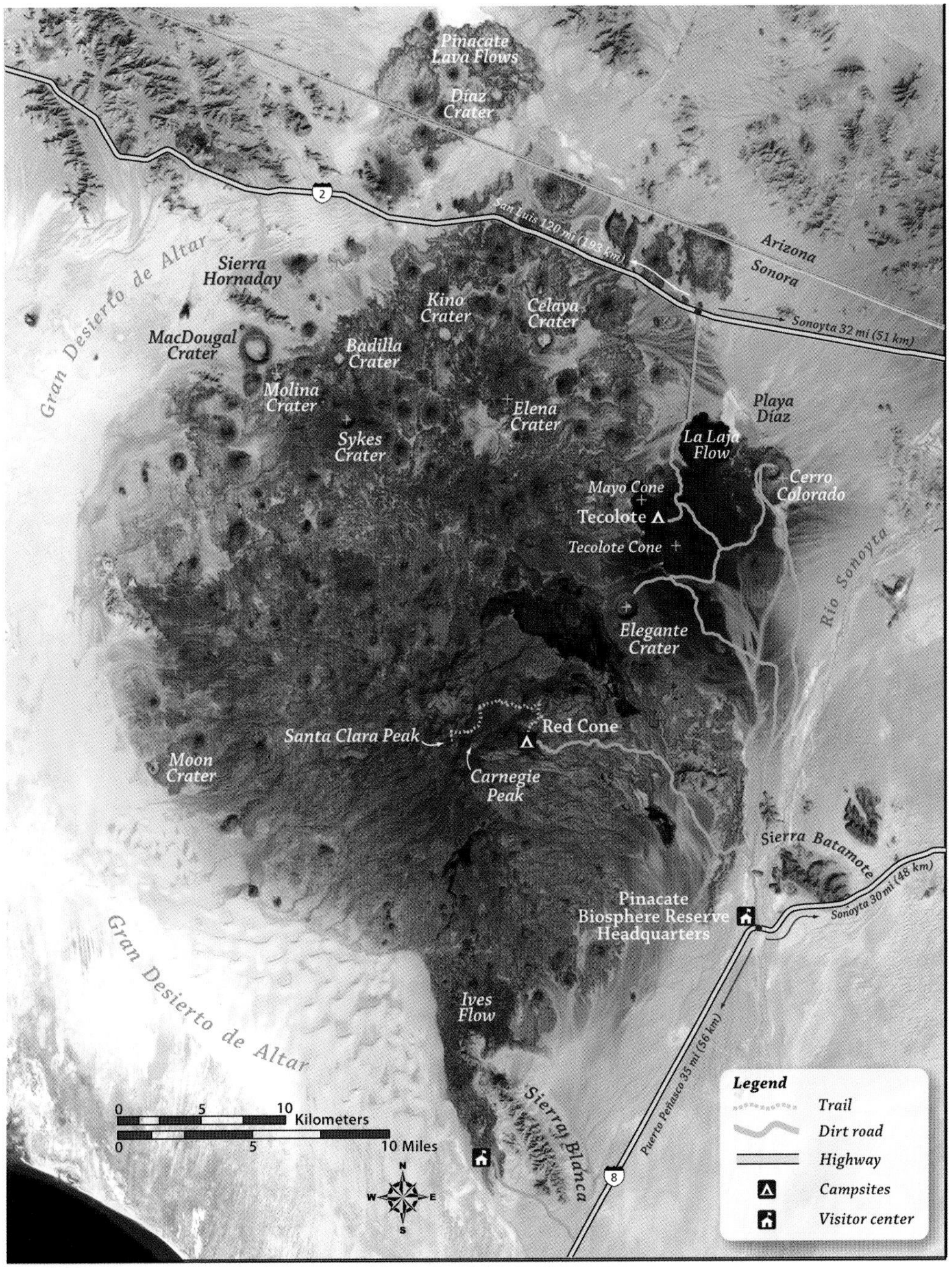

A SHIELD VOLCANO IS A THICK PILE OF LAVA FLOWS, USUALLY BASALT, PILED ONE ATOP THE OTHER LIKE A LAYER CAKE. OVER TIME THESE FORM A LARGE, GENTLY SLOPING MOUNTAIN RESEMBLING A GIANT FALLEN WARRIOR'S SHIELD.

DUE TO THE HIGH SEDIMENT CONTENT OF THE COLORADO RIVER, EARLY SETTLERS SAID THE WATER WAS "TOO THICK TO DRINK, AND TOO THIN TO PLOW."

Gran Desierto de Altar

The Pinacate volcanic field is inundated on the west by a sea of shifting sand dunes—the Gran Desierto de Altar, meaning "the great desert shrine." This is the largest "active" dune field in North America, covering about 4,800 square miles (12,400 km^2).[18] Virtually all of the sand in the Gran Desierto derives from the ancient Colorado River Delta and the upper Gulf of California, material carried to the area by prevailing westerly winds during the last tens of thousands of years.[19] In fact, rocks eroded from the Grand Canyon in northern Arizona were the source for much of this sand—a thought that evokes the marvel of geologic processes.

Gulf of California

The Gulf of California (hereafter called the gulf) lies along the western edge of the Gran Desierto. Some early explorers called it *El Mar Vermejo,* or the Vermilion Sea, perhaps after the color of the water caused by "red tides" (red-pigmented phyto- or zooplankton) or, more likely, after the reddish color of suspended sediment in water entering from the Colorado River. It was later called the *Mar de Cortés,* or Sea of Cortez, after the Spanish conquistador Hernando Cortés, who conquered central Mexico in 1521 and sent

GRAN DESIERTO NEAR MOON CRATER. Photo by Peter L. Kresan

THE UPPER GULF OF CALIFORNIA EXPERIENCES ONE OF THE HIGHEST TIDAL FLUCTUATION AMPLITUDES IN THE WORLD, POSSIBLY SECOND ONLY TO THE BAY OF FUNDY IN CANADA. DURING THE HIGHEST SPRING TIDES AT PUERTO PEÑASCO, THE FLUCTUATION IS ABOUT 24 FEET (7 M) BETWEEN HIGH AND LOW TIDES; IN THE COLORADO RIVER DELTA IT IS POSSIBLY 30 FEET (9 M) AT THE SAME TIMES.

ships under the command of the navigator Francisco de Ulloa to explore the upper gulf coast in 1539.[20]

The Colorado River supplied the upper gulf with a substantial influx of nutrient-rich freshwater until the construction of retention dams in the 1930s. Its watershed drains portions of seven states—Arizona, California, New Mexico, Nevada, Colorado, Wyoming, and Utah. It covers about 242,000 square miles (625,000 km^2) in the United States and about 3,000 square miles (7,770 km^2) in the Mexican states of Baja California and Sonora. The Colorado River, including its chief tributary, the northern Green River, is about 1,700 miles (4,400 km) long and historically drained eight to ten percent of the total U.S. watershed. Today, all water from the river is diverted for agricultural and municipal use in the United States and Mexico; there is no allotted flow into the gulf.

Sonoyta River

The Río Sonoyta lies on the eastern side of the Sierra Pinacate. Thousands of years ago, this river flowed south into the upper gulf, creating the Morua and La Pinta estuaries *(esteros)* east of Puerto Peñasco. A typical estuary is a shallow embayment with freshwater runoff and ocean saltwater mixing at the mouth of a river flowing into the sea; however, as with many other estuaries in the gulf, Morua and La Pinta are "negative estuaries," meaning that freshwater is no longer flowing into them with any regularity.

Historically, surface water in the Río Sonoyta flowed south to the Sierra Batamote, near the reserve's current biological field station; today, however, perennial water flows only in patches west of the Mexican border town of Sonoyta. Its surface flows reach the gulf only rarely, almost exclusively limited to *El Niño* years associated with heavy rains and floods in the American Southwest.

The Río Sonoyta may have formerly flowed farther west across the northern part of the Pinacate volcanic field and drained into the upper gulf at Adair Bay (*Bahía Adair*),[22] a possibility suggested by the distribution of volcanic craters formed by the explosive mingling of molten lava with groundwater. Permeable, water-saturated gravels deposited along this ancient river course may have provided the groundwater needed to form these craters.

"SONOYTA" IN O'ODHAM MEANS "AT THE FOOT OF THE ROUNDED HILL."[21]

SONOYTA.
Organ Pipe Cactus National Monument

PERENNIAL REACH OF RIO SONOYTA.
Organ Pipe Cactus National Monument

FRESHWATER ARTESIAN SPRINGS[23] AND DEPOSITS OF THE FRESHWATER MINERAL TRONA,[24] DOT THE SHORELINE OF ADAIR BAY. ABOUT 125,000 YEARS AGO, DURING A SEA LEVEL HIGHSTAND, THE EL BORRASCOSO COQUINA REEF FORMED JUST OFFSHORE WHERE FRESHWATER MET THE SEA.[25] A FRESHWATER CHANNEL MAY ONCE HAVE DRAINED INTO THIS AREA, AND REMNANTS OF WATER FLOWING IN THE NOW SAND-COVERED CHANNEL OF THE ANCIENT RÍO SONOYTA MAY STILL APPEAR AS ARTESIAN SPRINGS. ANOTHER POSSIBILITY IS THAT THE EXISTING FRESHWATER PRESENCE ULTIMATELY DERIVES FROM THE COLORADO RIVER AND IS CHANNELED TO THIS AREA BY SUBSURFACE FAULTS ALONG THE UPPER GULF.

MORUA ESTUARY. Larry Marshall

TIDAL CHANNELS AT ADAIR BAY. Photo courtesy Organ Pipe Cactus National Monument

MALE PUPFISH DURING BREEDING SEASON.
John Rinne, Arizona-Sonora Desert Museum

DESERT PUPFISH (*Cyprinodon macularius*) tolerate high water salinity. This relict species still swims in the shallow El Doctor wetlands on the eastern side of the Colorado River Delta and in a few of the southernmost tributaries of the Colorado River, such as the ponds at the geothermal field of Cerro Prieto. A closely related species, the Sonoyta pupfish (*C. eremus*), is found in the intermittent ponds of the Río Sonoyta and just across the border in Quitobaquito Spring in Organ Pipe Cactus National Monument.[26] Ancestral populations of these two species may have once been in contact if the ancient Río Sonoyta did, indeed, empty into Adair Bay and/or the El Doctor wetlands. At that time there would likely have existed a single species, which—following isolation caused by the shift in course of the Río Sonoyta—subsequently evolved into the two species we know today. Based on "molecular clocks," which allow scientists to estimate rates of genetic change between populations of living organisms, the divergence of *Cyprinodon macularius* and *C. eremus* occurred between 1.9 and 1.1 million years ago.[27] This is approximately the same age (1.7 to 1.1 million years ago) as the earliest dated volcanism in the Pinacate. The northern volcanic flows may have blocked and diverted the western course of the ancient Río Sonoyta, causing it to shift southward to its historical route to the gulf, forming the Morua and La Pinta estuaries, and isolating these populations of pupfish from each other.

QUITOBAQUITO SPRINGS AND POND. Organ Pipe Cactus National Monument

Sierra Blanca

Located at the southern edge of the shield volcano, the Sierra Blanca is a white mountain range visible on the west side of the highway between Sonoyta and Puerto Peñasco. The distinctively pale range vividly contrasts with the dark Pinacate volcanics. The Sierra Blanca is composed of ancient granite approximately 1.4 billion years old,[28] which uplifted from beneath the Earth's surface during the Basin and Range Disturbance between 20 and 8 million years ago. Beginning about 20 million years ago, the Earth's crust in the southwestern United States and northwestern Mexico pulled apart and fractured along steeply dipping faults, resulting in the formation of mountain ranges with deep basins between them. Over time, the uplifted mountains eroded and their sediments slowly filled the basins. The Basin and Range Province formed largely as a result of the collapse of the basins relative to the ranges, and subsequent infilling of the basins, rather than uplift of the ranges alone relative to sea level. The Basin and Range Disturbance ended about 8 million years ago, although recurrent earthquakes during historical time signal that some faults are still active.[29]

SIERRA BLANCA LOOKING NW, WITH IVES FLOW AND GRAN DESIERTO TO UPPER LEFT. Organ Pipe Cactus National Monument (left)

WEST SIDE OF SIERRA BLANCA, IVES FLOW AT BASE, FROM GRAN DESIERTO.
Bill Glass

WEST SIDE OF SIERRA BLANCA WITH IVES FLOW IN FOREGROUND. Bill Glass

SIERRA BLANCA FROM WEST EDGE OF IVES FLOW (FOREGROUND). Bill Glass

GEOLOGY

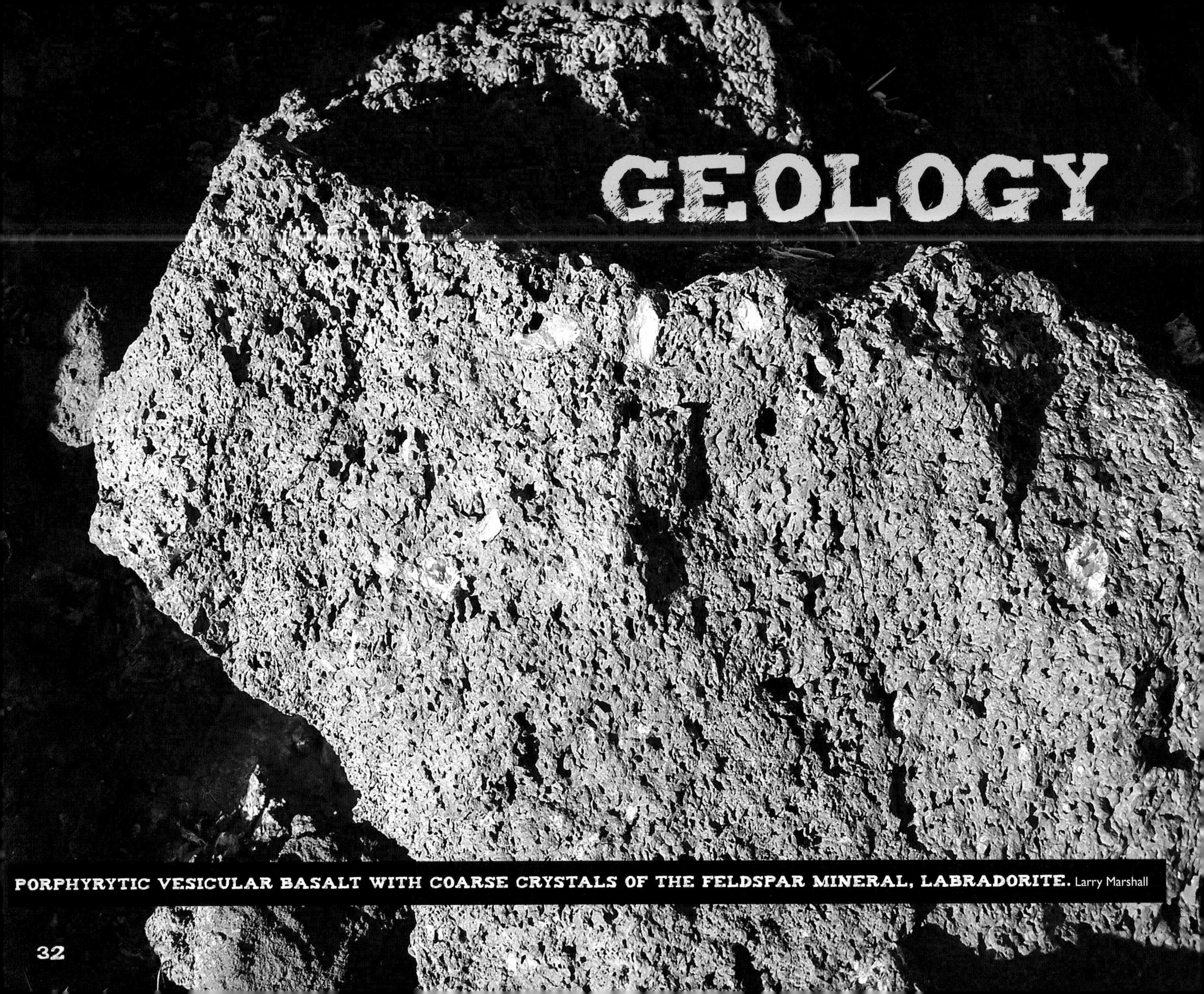

PORPHYRYTIC VESICULAR BASALT WITH COARSE CRYSTALS OF THE FELDSPAR MINERAL, LABRADORITE. Larry Marshall

SOME BASALTS CONTAIN NUMEROUS SMALL HOLES, OR "VESICLES," WHERE GAS BUBBLES WERE PRESENT AT THE TIME OF THEIR ERUPTION. THEY ARE CALLED VESICULAR BASALTS.

Sierra Pinacate

The Sierra Pinacate is mostly a huge, extinct shield volcano, as described earlier. The accumulation of hundreds or thousands of lava flows, mainly of the type geologists call basalt, built this volcano. Basalts are typically dark gray to black in color and contain about 50% silicon dioxide (silica) and some 10% each of iron, magnesium, and calcium oxides. Many basalts of the Pinacate contain relatively abundant alkaline metals as well, including oxides of sodium and potassium. As a result, they are called alkali basalts.

Most of these basalts can be further described as "porphyritic" alkali basalts because they contain large crystals called "phenocrysts" in their fine-grained gray matrix, somewhat like chocolate chunks in a chocolate chip cookie. Some of these are crystals of labradorite, a kind of feldspar mineral; the labradorite crystals can be either creamy white or very pale citrine and translucent, like fragments of broken glass. Other crystals in Pinacate basalts are yellowish olive-green grains of the mineral olivine.

Cinder Cones, Lava Flows, and Giant Craters

Following the long period in which the shield volcano formed, new sources of magma were generated below the Earth's crust. The resulting eruptions formed widespread cinder cones, lava flows, and giant craters.

Cinder Cones. About 400 cinder cones are visible in the Pinacate, many of which lie upon the older shield volcano. Only a few have been named, and most are inaccessible by road. Most were formed by eruptions lasting from a few weeks or months to years. Because of their high gas content, these cones erupted small fragments of ash and cinders, as well as larger chunks called volcanic bombs, made of

SANTA CLARA (UPPER) AND CARNEGIE (LOWER, REDDISH COLOR) CONES. Organ Pipe Cactus National Monument

MAGMA IS MOLTEN ROCK IN THE INTERIOR OF THE EARTH. IT CAN GIVE RISE TO VOLCANIC ERUPTIONS AT THE SURFACE. WITH TIME, THE MAGMA CHAMBER BENEATH A SHIELD VOLCANO CAN BECOME MORE AND MORE SILICEOUS AND POORER IN IRON AND MAGNESIUM AS IRON-RICH CRYSTALS FORM FROM THE MAGMA AND SINK TO THE BOTTOM OF THE CHAMBER. WE KNOW THIS HAPPENED AT VOLCÁN EL PINACATE BECAUSE THE YOUNGER FLOWS OF THE SHIELD VOLCANO ARE LIGHTER IN COLOR, INDICATING A LOWER IRON CONTENT AND HIGHER CONTENT OF SILICA, SODIUM, AND POTASSIUM. FOUND NEAR THE TOP OF THE OLD SHIELD, THESE LIGHT-COLORED LAVAS ARE CALLED "TRACHYTE."

CLUSTER OF YOUNG CINDER CONES WITH SHARP ANGLES OF REPOSE AND DEEP, BOWL-LIKE SUMMIT CRATERS. Photo by Peter L. Kresan

CINDER CONES. Bill Glass

MUD CRACKS IN CINDER CONE CRATER PLAYA NW OF SYKES CRATER. Bill Glass basaltic material. The ejected rocks formed steep-sided cones, some hundreds of feet high.

Ash (*ceniza*) is a term used for dust and very small volcanic fragments. Cinders (*morusa*) are frothy volcanic fragments 0.1 to 2.5 inches (2 to 64 mm) across. (Because they are so light and uniform in size, cinders are highly desirable as a road construction material and were mined for this purpose.) Volcanic bombs, usually a few inches to several feet long, are typically found very near the site of eruption. Cinders and bombs are usually dark gray to black, but may also be a reddish color due to oxidation of their iron content; basically, they are rusted. The ash, cinders, and bombs are collectively called pyroclastic (meaning fire-broken) ejecta, a term which refers to materials of all sizes blown out during a volcanic eruption.

Cinder cones generally have central craters, which vary in size and depth. These craters become less well defined as the cones erode and their original shapes are altered. When the cone is new, the layers of pyroclastic cinder that make up its sides lie at an "angle of repose"—the steepest slope at which the loose cinders will rest without sliding down. This angle is constant, depending on the material, and will not change regardless of the cone's size. For example, salt poured in a pile will also have a consistent angle of repose, whether the pile is two inches (5 cm) or 200 feet (60 m) high. Sand dunes also have an angle of repose that is consistent for the size of the loose sand grains. Every substance of a particular grain size and roughness has its own angle of repose. The well-preserved Mayo Cone just north of El Tecolote campground

CINDER CONE CRATER NW OF SYKES CRATER. Bill Glass

has an angle of repose of about 30°. With time, erosion modifies the shape of the cone and the original angle of repose is no longer evident.

Lava Flows. Basalt lava flows are grouped into two types: "pahoehoe" and "aa." Of Hawaiian origin, these terms apply to the flow surface. Some young Pinacate flows look as if they poured out and hardened just yesterday.

Pahoehoe (pronounced pa-hoy-hoy) flows have smooth, ripplelike surfaces and are easy to walk upon. The ripples often form textures like sinuous ropes, and the flows are sometimes called ropy pahoehoe or simply ropy lava. The ripples are formed perpendicular to the direction of the flow. This type of flow was relatively nonviscous, like molasses, during eruption.

The Italy-shaped Ives Flow is a good example of a young pahoehoe flow. It occurs at the southern end of the Pinacate, including the west side of the Sierra Blanca. The dunes of the Gran Desierto conceal its western margin, but the flow is exposed over some 17 square

IVES FLOW LOOKING NORTH.
Organ Pipe Cactus National Monument

PAHOEHOE IVES FLOW. Richard C. Brusca

PAHOEHOE IVES FLOW. Richard C. Brusca

miles (45 km^2), which is about 3% of the 580-square-mile (1,500-km^2) area of the volcanic field.[30] The Ives Flow, including that portion under the sands, is thought by some geologists to cover as much as 5% of the volcanic field.[31] The volume of lava in this flow is about one eighth of a cubic mile (0.5 km^3). The Ives Flow magma erupted through several long, parallel fissures at the Earth's surface, as opposed to a flow that issued from a single point source at the base or on the side of a cinder cone.[32]

Aa (pronounced ah-ah) flows are difficult to walk on because of the razor-sharp edges of broken basalt. As an aa flow gets farther from its source, the molten lava begins to cool and crystallize; it becomes brittle and breaks up to form sharp, jagged blocks. In Mexico, aa flows are sometimes called *chicharrones* (fried pork skins), because of their irregular surface texture. The flow from La Laja Cone, along the east side of the main north entrance road from Highway 2, is a good example of a young aa flow.

A lava flow typically erupts as a river of hot liquid rock from the base or side of a cinder cone. Flows can occur either synchronously with cinder eruptions or when gas

TECOLOTE AA FLOW. Photo by Peter L. Kresan

COLLAPSED LAVA TUBE. Richard C. Brusca

pressure in the cinder cone eruption is low and the vent is no longer ejecting ash, cinders, and bombs.

Magma erupts at the Earth's surface through a vent. After eruptions, vents can be filled with solidified volcanic rock. If softer rock surrounding an old vent eventually erodes away to expose the lava-filled vent on the Earth's surface, that formation is called a "volcanic neck." Molten lava may continue to flow below a hardened upper crust as the surface of a lava flow cools and solidifies. After molten lava has drained out of the interior of a flow with a hardened outer surface, an elongate, empty cavity called a "lava tube" is left within the flow. Throughout the Pinacate, caves

LAVA TUBE CAVE ENTRANCE. Francis M. Harty

AN AA FLOW. Bill Glass

TECOLOTE CAMPGROUND WITH AA FLOW IN BACKGROUND. Organ Pipe Cactus National Monument

TECOLOTE AA FLOW. Bill Glass

HORNITO. © Arizona-Sonora Desert Museum. Mark Dimmitt

of all sizes originated as lava tubes, providing havens for animals, especially bats. They play an important role in O'odham creation lore.

Large masses of cinders, bombs, and even small dikes can be rafted out from the walls of Pinacate cinder cones on flows that open breaches in their walls.

H*ornitos* (little ovens) are small spatter cones on flows, created when ejected molten rock falls on the flow surface.

TECOLOTE FLOW. Painting by José Castelao

Giant Craters. The most spectacular features of the Pinacate volcanic field are its giant craters—great circular basins caused by volcanic eruptions. They typically range from a quarter-mile to a mile (400 to 1,600 m) in diameter and from 50 to 800 feet (15 to 244 m) deep. Each has its own character and personality.

A detailed study of Crater Elegante[33] suggests that rising magma reacting violently with underground water caused steam-blast explosions of short duration, much like a repeatedly exploding pressure-cooker.[34] Numerous old lava flows can be seen in the walls of many of the Pinacate craters, and these acted as part of the lid on the pressure cooker. The original vent at Crater Elegante was much smaller in diameter than the present crater, which could not have formed simply as a result of steam explosions blowing a big hole in the ground. Instead, repeated steam explosions at Elegante gradually removed underlying loose sediments from beneath the stack of old lava flows. The roof of the resulting subterranean cavity collapsed, creating a particularly large crater.

Volcanic craters that form as magma interacts explosively with groundwater, like Elegante, are known as "maars" (German for "crater lakes"). Some of the largest maar craters in North America are found in the Pinacate, and eight of the twelve craters in the volcanic field are regarded as maars.[35]

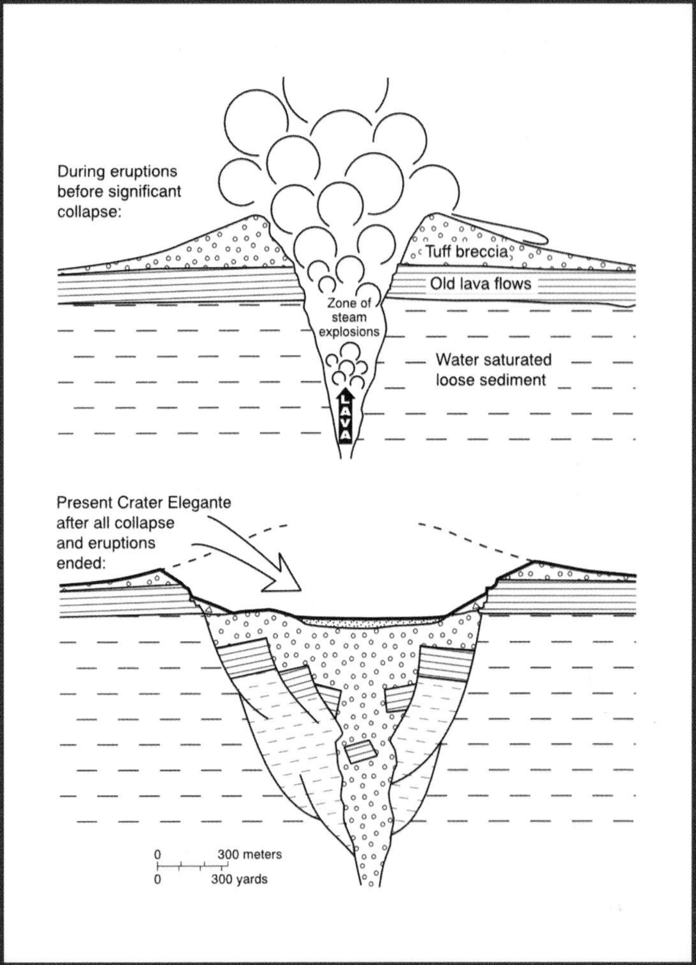

VERTICAL, CUTAWAY VIEW OF CRATER ELEGANTE AS IT MAY HAVE APPEARED DURING ERUPTIONS (TOP) AND AS SEEN TODAY FOLLOWING ERUPTIONS AND COLLAPSE TO FORM THE PRESENT CRATER (BELOW). See Bezy, Gutmann and Haxel, 2000, p. 52, for details. Illustration by James T. Gutmann, Arizona Geological Survey.

These maars share common characteristics. They have floors that lie below the former ground surface, and they are typically rimmed by tuff breccias. Tuff is the fine sediment that forms when volcanic ash falls back to the Earth's surface. It is typically white but can be gray, yellow, or red. Tuff "breccia" is a deposit of ash and larger volcanic fragments mixed with older rocks and sediments brought up from below the Earth's surface during eruption. It is analogous to concrete, which contains rocks of various sizes bound together in a matrix.

TUFF BRECCIA AROUND RIM OF CERRO COLORADO. Larry Marshall

The other four giant craters in the reserve do not fall into "maar" or other neat categories of volcanoes, but at the time of their formation they also probably had an aquifer-steam-driven component.[36]

The basalt cliffs that typically form the walls of the maars are nearly vertical. (It is dangerous to enter these craters, and even researchers must obtain permission from reserve authorities to do so.) Their floors are flat, filled with whitish silt and other fine-grained sediments, and show remnants of small playa lakes near their centers. The inner craters are encircled by a ring of talus, an apron of angular boulders broken from the surrounding crater walls.[37]

The Pinacate Craters

The diameters and depths of the craters provided here are based on previous reports and/or on observations by the authors; most crater measurements have yet to be confirmed and their names standardized.[38] This listing includes all the giant craters in the Pinacate volcanic field.

BADILLA CRATER: Diameter 1,150 feet (350 m), depth 35 feet (11 m). Named for Alfredo Badilla Martínez of Sonoyta, although Badilla is sometimes misspelled "Badillo." It is locally called Volcán Tinajita.

BADILLA CRATER. Bob Sharp

CARAVAJALES CRATER: Diameter 1,200 feet (366m), depth 30 feet (9m). Named for Juan Caravajales, the last Hia C'ed O'odham to live in this area.[39] In the past, it has also been called Hayden Crater for the archaeologist Julian Hayden.[40] Hartmann called this crater "Hayden/Caravajales."[41] It was discovered in the winter of 1963. Tuff breccia is lacking in the crater rim, and it is not a maar crater.[42]

CELAYA CRATER: Mean diameter 3,280 feet (1,000m), depth 260 feet (79 m). Named for Alberto Celaya of Sonoyta.[43] It is also known as Volcán los Vidrios (vidrios means "pieces of glass").

CERRO COLORADO: Diameter 2,460 feet (750 m), depth 300 feet (100 m). The name Cerro Colorado has long been used by residents of Sonoyta, cerro meaning "large hill" and colorado (reddish) referring to the color of the tuff that forms the crater's wall and rim. Geologists have suggested that the shape of this cerro may have developed as the result of predominantly northerly winds carrying the ash southward to build the high south rim of the crater during steam-blast eruptions. The site of the crater was not overlain by extensive older basalt flows at the time of eruption although the edge of one old flow is evident in the southwestern part of the crater near the foot of the cliffs. Cerro Colorado is regarded as a tuff cone, not a maar crater.[44]

CELAYA CRATER. Bill Glass

Photo by Peter L. Kresan

Bill Glass

CERRO COLORADO

Bob Sharp

DÍAZ CRATER: Diameter 2,624 feet (800 m), depth 0 feet. Named for the Spanish conquistador Melchior Díaz, possibly the first European to cross the western Sonoran Desert and the northern Pinacate volcanic field.[45] This low-lying crater, identified from satellite photographs, is located in the Cabeza Prieta National Wildlife Refuge just north of the Devil's Highway and the U.S.-Mexico border. Its rim lies at ground level, and whatever depression was there is now filled with wind-blown sand. It is probably a tuff ring, not a maar crater.[46]

CRATER ELEGANTE. Photo by Peter L. Kresan

CRATER ELEGANTE IN FAR DISTANCE, LOOKING EAST. Bill Glass

CRATER ELEGANTE: Mean diameter 5,100 feet (1,600 m) from rim crest to rim crest, depth 800 ft (244 m). Named by explorer Carl Lumholtz as a tribute to its preeminent depth and beauty among the Pinacate craters.[47] Elegante (meaning "elegant") is the largest crater in the reserve and the most frequently visited. This crater formed by explosive eruptions followed by collapse in which half of a large, old cinder cone in the area was destroyed. The remaining half of that cone, named Gutmann's Cone[48] by geologist Daniel Lynch, is still visible on the southeast side of the crater wall and rim. Elegante is the only crater known to have contained a large lake, evidenced by a "bathtub ring" of water-lain deposits about a quarter of the way up from the crater floor.[49] The lake was probably created by the ancient water table and not simply by infilling with rainwater.[50] Travertine in the water-lain sediments provided a carbon-14 date of about 17,200 carbon-14 years old.[51] This date was calibrated to a calendar age of about 20,250 years by geologist James Gutmann.[52] This age is consistent with the recent date of 32,000 years ago for the formation of the crater itself.[53]

CRATER ELEGANTE, LOOKING WEST. Bill Glass

CRATER ELENA: No diameter or depth has been published. Named by Daniel Lynch for his wife.[54] This is a cone built of cinders and tuff, not a maar crater.[55]

KINO CRATER: Diameter 2,620 feet (798 m), depth 65 feet (20 m). Named for Eusebio Francisco Kino, the Jesuit priest who visited the Pinacate on three occasions between 1698 and 1706.

MACDOUGAL CRATER: Mean diameter 5,300 feet (1,600 m) from rim to rim, depth 430 feet (131 m). Named by zoologist William Hornaday for Dr. Daniel MacDougal, botanist and director of the Desert Botanical Laboratory on Tumamoc Hill in Tucson, and a member of the 1907 Hornaday Expedition.[56] On one Mexican topographic map it is labeled as Volcán Verdugo. MacDougal is the second largest crater in the reserve.

SIERRA HORNADAY FROM MACDOUGAL CRATER. Bill Glass

MACDOUGAL CRATER. Bill Glass

MOLINA CRATER: Diameter 490 feet (149 m), depth 100 feet (30 m). Named by William Hornaday for Olegario Molina,[57] who served as Secretary of Development (Fomento) for President Díaz in the early twentieth century. Three obvious separate vents give this crater a distinctive cloverleaf shape. The southeastern vent is actually composed of two vents, making four visible vents. This crater is also known as Cloverleaf Crater and Volcán El Trébol.

MOLINA CRATER. Bob Sharp

MOLINA CRATER. Bill Glass

MOON CRATER: Diameter 1,480 feet (451 m), depth 75 feet (23 m). Reputedly discovered and named in the winter of 1956-1957 by Glenton Sykes, the son of Godfrey Sykes of the 1907 Hornaday Expedition.[58] Moon Crater, like many lunar craters, has a low central peak. It is also known as Crater La Luna, Volcán La Luna, Volcán El Sombrero, and Volcán de Chichi. In the 1940s, local resident Filiberto Pérez called it Volcán de Chichi in reference to the central cinder cone.[59] (Chichi is a Mexican slang word for a woman's breast.) This crater is unique in that it is a maar into which a cinder cone erupted. Numerous basalt boulders in the tuff breccia along the rim represents an earlier lava flow that is now largely covered with colluvium and sand from the adjacent Gran Desierto. (Colluvium is the loose sediment at the bottom of a slope that has tumbled or been washed down.)

MOON CRATER

Francis M. Harty

Photo by Peter L. Kresan

SYKES CRATER: Mean diameter 3,280 feet (1,000 m), depth 720 feet (219 m). Named by William Hornaday for Godfrey Sykes, an English soldier-of-fortune, explorer, engineer, and geographer on the Hornaday Expedition.[60] It is sometimes called Crater Grande and Volcán Romo, for Chico Romo, a Sonoyta rancher in the early twentieth century.[61] A large cinder cone that preceded the maar crater contributed to the extreme height of the present-day crater rim. Evidence of the cinder cone can be clearly seen on the north side of the crater wall and rim.

SYKES CRATER, LOOKING NORTH. Bill Glass

MACDOUGAL CRATER WITH SIERRA HORNADAY IN FOREGROUND (LOOKING SE). Photo by Peter L. Kresan

A DIKE IS A BASALT INTRUSION THAT CUTS ACROSS BEDDING PLANES (HORIZONTAL LAYERS OF ROCK OF ANY TYPE). IN CONTRAST, A SILL IS AN INTRUSION BETWEEN BEDDING PLANES. DIKES AND SILLS ARE BOTH VISIBLE IN THE PARTIAL CINDER CONE (GUTMANN'S CONE) ON THE SOUTHEAST WALL OF CRATER ELEGANTE.[65]

Age of the Pinacate Volcanic Field

Different methods are used to date volcanic rocks. The potassium-argon (K/Ar) method measures the isotopic ratio of potassium-40 to argon-40, and is normally used to date volcanic rocks older than 100,000 years. For volcanic rocks younger than this, the argon-argon (40Ar/39Ar) method is preferred. This technique can be used to date rocks 2,000 years old, but there is a large range of uncertainty (±) with very young rocks.

In the Pinacate volcanic field, geologist Daniel Lynch dated nine samples of alkali basalts, trachytes, and lavas of intermediate composition using the K/Ar method.[62] These dates range from 1.7 to 1.1 million years old. In addition, six samples from flows on both sides of the shield volcano, and one from a flow on the shield near Carnegie Peak gave ages of 1.2 million to 410,000 years.[63]

Flows within the walls of the Elegante, Moon, and MacDougal Craters have also been dated.[64] The lowest exposed flow in the wall of Crater Elegante dated to 460,000 years old. A flow pierced by the eruption of Moon Crater gave an age of 340,000 years, and a basalt dike formed at the time of the eruption in MacDougal Crater gave an age of 185,000 years.

The following list represents more recent dates by geologists James Gutmann and Brent Turrin using the 40Ar/39Ar method.[66] The symbol ± represents the range of uncertainty.

La Laja Flow: 12,000 ± 4,000 years. At the northeastern edge of the volcanic field, the cone that produced this flow became the Tezontle Mine, the area's largest cinder mine. It closed when the area became a biosphere reserve. Laja means, "slab" in Spanish.

Ives Flow: These workers report a 40Ar/39Ar age of 13,000 ± 3,000 years for this flow.[67]

Tecolote Cone: 27,000 ± 6,000 years. A flow on the north side of this cone was dated. Tecolote means "owl" in Nahuatl.

Crater Elegante: 32,000 ± 6,000 years. A flow contemporaneous with formation of the crater was dated.[68]

Carnegie Cone: 38,000 ± 8,000 years. The second highest peak in the Pinacate, this is a cinder cone formed atop the older shield volcano. A flow on the east side of the cone was dated.

Geologists continue to search for samples that will identify the oldest and the youngest flows. While we have few dated samples thus far, it is possible that new, and perhaps surprising, information about the area's volcanic history will emerge in the near future.

Radiometric dating utilizes the known rate at which radioactive isotopes decay to form new elements. Potassium-40 changes slowly into other elements, including argon. The age of a rock is estimated using this rate of change, and comparing the ratio of the parent isotope remaining to the derived isotope that has been produced by radioactive decay since the lava crystallized.

origin of the Pinacate Volcanic Field

To understand the origin of the volcanic activity, we must look at plate tectonic processes. Beginning about six million years ago, there was a major directional change in the movement of tectonic plates immediately to the west. The peninsula of Baja California, which had been part of the continental North American plate, was "captured" by the oceanic Pacific plate and began to move northward and westward away from what is today Sonora.[69] The Gulf of California developed at that time, and its seabed center became the new boundary between the Pacific and North American plates, with basaltic magma erupting along fractures in the floor of the gulf.

Because of the close proximity of the Pinacate volcanic field and the similar timing of volcanism, it is tempting to propose a genetic relationship between the volcanism in the two areas. However, there are two problems with this model. For one, the chemistry and mineralogy of the Pinacate volcanics are different from those of lavas erupted from oceanic spreading centers, such as occur in the Gulf of California.[70] A second problem involves the northwesterly orientation of the Gulf of California, which differs from the north-trending, dominant volcanic trends within the Pinacate.

As a result, some geologists have proposed that there is no relationship between the volcanism of these two adjacent areas. Instead, they suggest that there was a mantle plume or "hotspot" similar to, but smaller than, the one that produced the Hawaiian Islands chain.[71] Hotspots originate at great depth in the Earth's mantle and create linear volcanic chains that record the motion of the overlying plate. Evidence of such motion is not clear from the record of volcanism in the Pinacate. Nevertheless, other geologists have also suggested that the Pinacate may reflect a local "boil" in the mantle, somewhat akin to a hotspot but more localized in space and time, and more related to Basin and Range tectonics than to the spreading activity a short distance to the west.[72] Investigations of lava chemistry now under way should shed more light on this matter.

Volcanic Activity: Alive, Resting, or Dead?

The youngest dated volcanic activity in the reserve was 12,000 ± 4,000 years ago. In human history this was a long time ago, but in geological time it was only yesterday. There is no evidence of volcanic activity in the Pinacate today, nor is there documented evidence of activity since the arrival of Spaniards some 450 years ago. Therefore, the volcanic field is not considered "alive"; however, it is probably not "dead." Pinacate volcanism is best regarded as dormant or "resting." Volcanoes in the area will probably erupt again, but geologists cannot predict when.

PHYSICAL

Climate

Today the Pinacate has long hot summers and short cool winters. Maximum daily summer temperatures commonly range between 100° and 113°F (38° to 45°C) from late April to early October. At the time of publication, the highest temperature recorded for the Sonoran Desert was 134°F (56.7°C) taken in late June 1971 at Sierra Blanca in the Pinacate. Winter daytime temperatures often range between 60° and 75°F (15.5° to 24°C), while at night they may dip below freezing, with rare records of snowfall.[73]

TINAJA DE LOS PAPAGOS. Bob Sharp

Rainfall and Water Sources

Two unpredictable rainy seasons—a torrential summer monsoon, and a gentle winter-spring rain—bring relief to this parched land, where a rain gradient occurs from northeast (wettest) to southwest (driest). Sonoyta has the highest annual rainfall for the region, with 6.5 inches (164 mm), while Puerto Peñasco averages 5.9 inches (150 mm).[74]

ENVIRONMENT

Here, as in other locations in the Sonoran Desert, natural rock water tanks called *tinajas* collect rainfall. Tinajas are depressions scoured out of hard rock over tens of thousands of years by the force of torrential rainwater runoff and the sediment and debris it transports. Examples in the reserve include: Tinajas de los Papagos and de los Chivos on the west side; and Tinajas Lumholtz, de Carlina, Emilia, Romero, del Pinto, del Galletal, and del Cuervo on the east side.[75]

August is the best month to find water in tinajas, owing to the summer monsoon. The monsoon storms, which typically arrive in late June or early July, flush stagnant water and debris from the tinajas, providing a source of fresh water. However, August is also the hottest and most dangerous month to travel, especially if the monsoon arrives unusually late, or the storms are sparse. Tinajas were important water sources for native peoples and still are for wildlife today.

TINAJA DE LOS PAPAGOS. Julian Hayden, courtesy Stephen Hayden

Segments of the Río Sonoyta riverbed offer the only year-round surface water source known within the reserve, but the region also contains small freshwater artesian springs (*pozos*) along the coast of Adair Bay. As of 1993 the reserve also had about 120 drilled wells, used for limited agriculture, ranching, and drinking.[76]

Soils and other Surface Materials

Climate, surface cover, temperature, and water govern the types of plants and animals that are able to inhabit a given landscape, but the main limiting factor is the type of surface material and the amount of moisture it can hold. Six surface materials dominate the Pinacate reserve.

GRAN DESIERTO WEATHER STATION IN MARCH 2004 AFTER LOW WINTER RAINFALL (0.99 INCHES). Organ Pipe Cactus National Monument

GRAN DESIERTO WEATHER STATION IN MARCH 2005 AFTER HIGH WINTER RAINFALL (6.07 INCHES). Organ Pipe Cactus National Monument

Sand

The Gran Desierto is composed of shifting dunes that support little if any plant or animal life. Giant star dunes dominate the landscape, some rising to 600 feet (183 m) above the desert floor.[77] Sand holds rainwater and allows it to percolate to significant depths. However, it is low in mineral and organic nutrients sought by colonizing plants.

Around the desert's perimeter, stabilized sand dunes shift little, if at all, held in place by the roots of sparse vegetation. Diverse insects, reptiles, and small mammals live in these areas and leave numerous trackways in the soft sand that tell of their often-unseen abundance. Stabilized sand is easy to burrow into, and virtually all resident animals construct burrows or shady nests to escape daytime heat and nighttime cold.

TRACKWAYS IN GRAN DESIERTO SANDS. Larry Marshall

GRAN DESIERTO. Ami Pate

Volcanic Rock

The volcanic field is basically dark gray to black rock. Aa flows are covered with broken blocks filled with porous vesicles that trap and retain moisture. Lava blocks of various sizes create uneven ground surfaces that provide partial shade, which promotes the rooting of vegetation. The cavities, holes, and fissures make ideal perches for birds, and provide homes for insects, reptiles, and mammals.

When pahoehoe flows first form they resemble newly paved highways and are inhospitable to vegetation. Water runs off the relatively smooth surface, so plants cannot take root, while a lack of shade compounds the unfavorable conditions. Vegetation becomes established only after the flows crack and dust accumulates in crevices, a process that could take thousands of years. The cracking will sometimes expose lava tubes and create shady lava caves—ideal homes for insects, reptiles, and mammals (particularly bats).

Volcanic Cinders

Volcanic cinders invite colonization by plants. Cinders are filled with holes that trap moisture and collect wind-born dust and seeds within and between the loose rock particles. Once established, plant roots have ready access to the porous mineral-rich volcanic nuggets. The loose cinders, however, do not invite burrowing animals. For this reason, many of the smaller animals venture into the cinder plains only as visitors from surrounding lava flows until such time as a silt-rich soil develops on the cinders.

IN SAND FIELDS WHERE WIND DIRECTIONS ARE VARIABLE, DUNES CAN FORM WITH MULTIPLE "ARMS" TAILING OFF IN VARIOUS DIRECTIONS. THESE FORMS ARE CALLED "STAR DUNES."

Playas

Playas are very shallow, closed basins into which runoff collects temporarily, bringing with it silt and nutrients from surrounding areas. Windblown dust also collects, and a fine-grained soil quickly develops. The bottoms of many craters and the summit depressions of some cinder cones are mini-playas, where the fine-grained soil retains rainwater and supports short-lived ponds. Plants are seasonally abundant on crater floors, and the playas host some of the most spectacular wildflower displays in the Sonoran Desert. This soil also attracts burrowing animals, which can forage in the surrounding vegetation. The largest of the Pinacate playas, Playa Díaz, is located northwest of Cerro Colorado. It was named for the conquistador Melchior Díaz.

Desert Pavement

Found only in extremely arid landscapes, desert pavements form on flat areas devoid of vegetation. They are surfaces paved with a cobblestone-like layer of tightly interlocked pebbles, often coated with "rock varnish." Below the pebble surface is a fine-grained soil horizon composed of wind-blown silts and clays. This sediment,

A SOIL HORIZON IS A SINGLE LAYER OF EARTH THAT RUNS PARALLEL TO THE SURFACE AND IS DISTINCT IN ITS COMPOSITION OR CHARACTER FROM THE STRATA ABOVE AND BENEATH IT.

PLAYA DIAZ (UPPER LEFT) FROM CERRO COLORADO. Bill Glass

DESERT PAVEMENT. Larry Marshall

originally deposited on the surface of the pebbles, is carried by erosion and gravity to below the pebble pavement to form a soil layer. Once disturbed, desert pavements can take thousands of years to recover. For this reason, trails used thousands of years ago by early inhabitants are still clearly visible in areas where desert pavements prevail.[78] An excellent example of desert pavement runs along the north rim of Molina Crater.

Julian Hayden offers a vivid description of desert pavement:

> *Pavement formation depends on the occurrence of very severe and prolonged conditions of drought thousands of years in duration. During these climatic episodes of drought plants die, rodents disappear, and constant winds blow the loess* [fine sediments] *away. Stones in the soil, once mixed in by rodent activity around the plants, are dropped to a common level to form a tight mosaic. A layer of saline clay, from weathering of the basalt rock, develops just below this layer of stones, forming a surface mosaic, which prevents the regrowth of plants during succeeding wet climatic periods. For this reason pavements are essentially permanent, and any marks and disturbances of them by man are also permanent.*[79]

Rock varnish on desert pavement is a thin black, dark-brown, or reddish patina formed by the interaction of iron and manganese with bacteria on the surface of certain rocks. The layers develop very slowly, in some cases over tens of thousands of years. By removing desert varnish, native peoples created the symbols and figures etched into rock surfaces that we know as petroglyphs.[80]

ROCK VARNISH. Larry Marshall

Cryptobiotic crust

Cryptobiotic (meaning "of hidden life") soil or microphytic crusts are composed of cyanobacteria, algae, lichens, mosses, and liverworts. These small organisms help stabilize the soil, prevent erosion, fix nitrogen in the soil, and contribute nutrients to other plants. They form living crusts on some desert surfaces. These soils look like black mats during their dormant phase, but turn into green carpets when the soil is wetted and awakened after a rain. The crusts stay green for a few days, and then return to their dark dormant color. These soils are particularly sensitive to ground disturbance and, when disrupted, take decades to hundreds of years to recover.[81]

BIOLOGY

The Pinacate area supports a remarkable biological diversity, including: about 500 species of vascular plants, thousands of species of invertebrates, 2 species of native freshwater fishes, 4 species of native amphibians, 44 species of native reptiles, 237 species of resident and migratory birds, and 38 species of native mammals.[82]

Plants

Fifteen thousand years ago, after the end of the last southward influx of glaciers into what is now the northern United States, winters in the reserve were cooler and had more precipitation than today, while summers were also cooler but had little rain. Based on ancient climate data from samples in adjacent Arizona, higher-elevation portions of the Pinacate were probably blanketed by pinyon-juniper woodland and Joshua trees (*Yucca brevifolia*). This vegetation community is similar to those found today in cooler and wetter climates 150 miles (240 km) to the northwest in the Mojave Desert of southern California. Between 11,000 and 9,000 years ago, when summers were warmer and modern rainfall regimes began to develop, this vegetation community began to disappear from the Pinacate, retreating northward or to higher elevations.[83]

For most scientists, 9,000 years ago marks the "rebirth" of the Sonoran Desert, when plants we now associate with the Sonoran Desert began to appear. First came brittlebush and saguaro cactus, followed at different times by blue palo verde, foothills palo verde, ironwood, and organ pipe cactus. Desert vegetation comparable to that in the Sonoran Desert today probably developed during the many past interglacial warm periods, and today's desert community is similar to those established some eight million years ago.[84]

FOR MOST SCIENTISTS, 9,000 YEARS AGO MARKS THE "REBIRTH" OF THE SONORAN DESERT.

MOST PINACATE PLANTS HAVE LONG-LIVED SEEDS THAT ENABLE THEM TO SURVIVE UNPREDICTABLE RAINY SEASONS AND DEHYDRATING SUMMER HEAT.[86]

Much of what we know about prehistoric changes in climate and vegetation is based on the study of plant remains in ancient packrat (*Neotoma* sp.) middens, a term borrowed from archaeologists for "refuse piles." Packrats are large rodents that construct their houses in open areas and their dens in rock shelters, building with various local sticks, cactus stems, and anything else they find useful. The better or more secure house or den sites are used for many generations. These structures are often erroneously called nests, but the real nests are tiny fibrous structures in specialized chambers inside the house or den.

Packrats are herbivores that eat a great variety of plants. In rock shelters, hard, dark organic deposits may form on ledges or in crevices away from the main den, and these are preserved as long as they remain dry. Here, over time, bits and pieces of plants dropped by the packrats become cemented into the middens by rodent urine, and these midden assemblages reflect decades of vegetation the rodents ate or carried near the rock shelter—providing modern researchers with detailed glimpses of past vegetation and climate. Scientists have sampled hundreds of packrat middens, carbon-14 dated organic material, and identified the associated plant remains. Using this approach, they have compiled a well-dated record of plant communities in the Sonoran Desert for the past 40,000 years.[85]

For cactus lovers, the Pinacate is a Mecca in both diversity and sheer numbers, though many of these spiny plants occur only in patches. A visitor will see three species of giant cacti side-by-side: the saguaro (*Carnegiea gigantea*), organ pipe (*Stenocereus thurberi*), and senita (*Lophocereus schottii*).

PACK RAT. Tom Van Devender, Arizona-Sonora Desert Museum

ORGAN PIPE.
Arizona-Sonora Desert Museum

SAGUAROS.
©Arizona-Sonora Desert Museum. Mark Dimmitt.

SENITA.
Bill Glass

Several species of barrel cacti thrive here, including the red-spined California fire barrel (*Ferocactus cylindraceus*) and the photogenic many-headed barrel (*Echinocactus polycephalus*). There are also forests of the untouchable teddy bear cholla (*Cylindropuntia bigelovii*). At higher elevations, the thick-trunked, white-barked elephant tree (*Bursera microphylla*)—also known as torote or copal—grows abundantly.

The honey mesquite tree (*Prosopis glandulosa*) is the most conspicuous and predictable large perennial in the reserve.[88]

FIRE BARREL AND FIRE BARREL FLOWERS. Francis M. Harty

TEDDY BEAR CHOLLA. Arizona-Sonora Desert Museum

Other common perennials include: blue palo verde (*Parkinsonia florida*), desert ironwood (*Olneya tesota*), creosotebush (*Larrea tridentata*), slimleaf ragweed (*Ambrosia confertiflora*), spiny poppy (*Argemone gracilenta*), white bursage (*Ambrosia dumosa*), rattlesnake weed (*Euphorbia albomarginata*), devil's claw (*Proboscidea althaefolia*), brittlebush (*Encelia farinosa*), and the striking ocotillo (*Fouquieria splendens*), which can produce bright-red flowers six or more times a year.

MANY-HEADED BARREL CACTUS CLUSTERS CAN REACH 5 FEET (1.5 M) ACROSS, 3 FEET (1 M) IN HEIGHT, AND HAVE HUNDREDS OF HEADS.[87]

TEDDY BEAR CHOLLA FOREST.
Bill Glass

ELEPHANT TREE. Arizona-Sonora Desert Museum

MANY-HEADED BARREL.
Bill Glass

O'ODHAM USE FIBERS FROM THE SEED-BEARING POD OF THE DEVIL'S CLAW AS THE BLACK COLOR IN THEIR TRADITIONAL BASKETS.

Some plants with restricted ranges in the Pinacate area include: Wiggin's croton (*Croton wigginsii*), tansy spectaclepod (*Dimorphocarpa pinnatifida*), dune spurge (*Euphorbia platysperma*), golden aster (*Heterotheca thiniicola*), Pinacate ragwort (*Senecio pinacatensis*), Schott's wirelettuce (*Stephanomeria schottii*), seepweed (*Suaeda puertopenascoa*), desert chia (*Salvia columbariae*), and big galleta grass (*Hilaria rigida*).

Creosotebush forms nearly pure stands on sandy soils around the lava fields and Gran Desierto. A plant ascribed with medicinal qualities, it is the most drought-tolerant perennial plant in North America and among the longest-lived. Scientists estimate that one extended creosote ring in the Mohave Desert has survived more than 11,000 years. The O'odham claim creosote is their "drugstore" and was the first plant created.[89]

DEVILS CLAW SEED. John Bridges

PINACATE AND CREOSOTE. Organ Pipe Cactus National Monument

DESERT VERBENA. Organ Pipe Cactus National Monument

SOME OF THE PLANT COMMUNITIES...ARE DISTINCTIVE AND EASILY RECOGNIZED. THE WATER-POOR CREOSOTEBUSH COMMUNITY IS ONE. ALMOST PURE STANDS OF CREOSOTEBUSH SPARSELY COVER THE SANDY PLAINS SURROUNDING THE LAVA FIELD, CREATING A SEA OF LOW SHRUBS AROUND A VOLCANIC ISLAND. ALTHOUGH INDIVIDUAL CREOSOTEBUSHES MAY BE SEEN ELSEWHERE, THE CREOSOTEBUSH COMMUNITY STOPS QUITE ABRUPTLY WHEN THE SOIL CHANGES FROM SAND TO LAVA ROCK.[90]

GILA WOODPECKER. Paul Berquist

GILA WOODPECKERS (*MELANERPES UROPYGIALIS*) AND GILDED FLICKERS (*COLAPTES CHRYSOIDES*) MAKE THEIR NEST-HOLE CAVITIES IN SAGUARO CACTUS. THE EXPOSED TISSUE IN THE FRESH HOLE HEALS OVER LIKE A SCAB, FORMING WALLS FOR A COOL SHELTER. OTHER BIRDS, INCLUDING THE ELF OWL (*MICRATHENE WHITNEYI*), OFTEN USE NESTING CAVITIES ABANDONED BY THEIR BUILDERS. WHEN THE SAGUARO DIES AND DECOMPOSES, THE ROT-RESISTANT NEST CAVITIES THAT REMAIN INTACT ARE CALLED "DESERT BOOTS."

ELF OWL. Lewis Wayne Walker, Arizona-Sonora Desert Museum

After drenching winter rains, crater floors explode with orange flower carpets of annual globemallow (*Sphaeralcea coulteri*).[91] Summer rains bring ephemerals dominated by amaranth (*Amaranthus palmeri*) and lizardtail (*Gaura parviflora*), as well as a perennial ragweed (*Ambrosia confertiflora*).

The observant visitor may see the now rare camote or sand root (*Pholisma sonorae*) in the shifting sands of the Gran Desierto (not in the craters themselves). O'odham and other native peoples once relished the camote stem as a flavorful food. The O'odham call it *hia tadk* or dune root.[92]

Approximately ten percent of the plants recorded in the Pinacate area consist of non-native species.[93] Introduced from elsewhere in the world, the majority of these plants are unwanted agricultural or urban weeds, many of which outcompete and

DESERT BOOT. John Bridges

GLOBEMALLOW. Bill Glass

GILDED FLICKER. Paul and Shirley Berquist, Arizona-Sonora Desert Museum

FLOWERS IN GRAN DESIERTO. Ami Pate

replace native species. Among the most invasive are red brome (*Bromus rubens*), buffelgrass (*Pennisetum ciliare*), Mediterranean grass (*Schismus arabicus*), and Sahara mustard (*Brassica tournefortii*).[94]

Given the number of columnar cacti, it is not surprising that "nurse trees" are especially prevalent in the Pinacate. Visitors will frequently see a tree, usually a palo verde, providing protection for one or more senita, saguaro, or organ pipe cacti growing under it. Birds roost in the tree branches and deposit droppings that often include seeds eaten only hours earlier. The trees provide shade and nutrients for the seeds to germinate, and the baby cacti prosper. This relationship between nurse trees and cacti lasts for many years; but when the cacti mature and need more water, their roots usually outcompete those of the nurse trees for the meager moisture in the soil, so the nurse tree eventually dies. Examples of all stages of this life-giving and life-taking association between trees and cacti are abundant throughout the reserve.

SCHOTT'S WIRELETTUCE.
Jim Rorabaugh

FOREST OF CAMOTE.
Jim Rorabaugh

CAMOTE.
Jim Rorabaugh

PINACATE MOONLIGHT. Bill Glass

FLOWERS ON SIDE OF SIERRA PINACATE. Francis M. Harty

Tom Sharp

Bill Glass

Animals

Invertebrates

Invertebrates—a category that includes insects, worms, snails, and many other spineless creatures—are the most diverse group of animals in the Pinacate, in both numbers and species. However, most go unnoticed unless attention is drawn to them by their color, beauty, or the potential threat of being bitten or stung.

The namesake invertebrate of the reserve is the charismatic, black Pinacate beetle (*Eleodes armata*). Like the many species of *Eleodes*, this beetle emits a foul-smelling chemical from glands near the tip of its abdomen as a defense strategy. Before they do, however, they warn would-be attackers by elevating their tail end into the air, appearing to "stand on their head." Most animals will not prey on *Eleodes*, or will only try once. However, the tiny southern grasshopper mouse (*Onychomys torridus*) has learned to quickly thrust the abdomen of this beetle into the sand, and then feed leisurely on the rest of the body from the head down.

The most commonly seen ants are the harvester and desert leaf-cutter. Harvester ants (*Pogonomyrmex* sp.) are important consumers and dispersers of seeds. Their nests are easily recognized because they clear the entrance area of plants to limit competition for soil moisture. Desert leafcutter ants (*Acromyrmex versicolor)* make trails that can range up to 600 feet (182 m) from the nest. Ant colonies are comprised chiefly of females, one or more queens, and many workers. Workers collect food, care for larvae, and protect the colony. Only the queen produces eggs. Periodically, usually during summer monsoons, colonies produce winged males and females called *alates* that start new colonies. In most ant species, queens store sperm during the nuptial flight (as alates) for the twenty-year or more lifetime of the colony, making queen ants some of the longest-lived insects.

Velvet ants (*Dasymutilla* sp.) are attractive red, yellow, or silver-haired creatures. They are not really ants, but wingless female wasps. Visitors to the reserve may be tempted to pick them up, but are advised to refrain, because they have a very painful sting. Paper

GRASSHOPPER MOUSE.
Paul & Shirley Berquist, Arizona-Sonora Desert Museum

wasps (*Polistes* sp.) and tarantula hawks (*Pepsis* sp.) are also common here. Females of both species can sting, and the venom of tarantula hawks packs the most painful wasp sting in North America. As their common name implies, female *Pepsis* wasps sting tarantulas, attacking a vulnerable spot at the joint between their leg and body. This paralyzes, but does not kill the tarantula, which the wasp then drags into a burrow where she deposits a single egg on the body of the incapacitated spider. The tarantula serves as food for the larval wasp prior to its emergence as a flying adult.

Two of the Pinacate's most impressive invertebrates are the giant desert centipede (*Scolopendra heros*) and giant desert millipede (*Orthoperus ornatus*). The giant desert centipede is strictly nocturnal. Its black and orange coloration reminds potential predators that its venom-injecting first legs (called "gnathopods") deliver a powerful sting. Centipedes

DESERT CENTIPEDE.
Arizona-Sonora Desert Museum

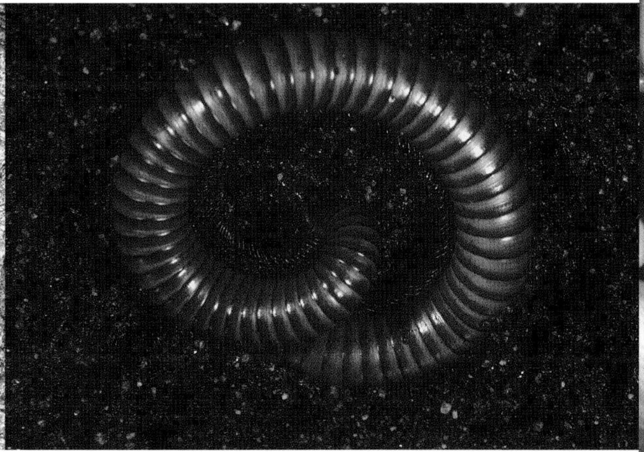

GIANT DESERT MILLIPEDE.
Arizona-Sonora Desert Museum

TARANTULA HAWK.
Arizona-Sonora Desert Museum

STRIPED TAIL SCORPION. Paul & Shirley Berquist. Courtesy of Arizona-Sonoran Desert Museum.

POLLINATORS ARE CRUCIAL TO THE SURVIVAL OF MOST PLANTS, MOVING POLLEN FROM THE ANTHER OF ONE FLOWER TO THE STIGMA OF ANOTHER. POLLEN IS THE POWDERY SUBSTANCE MADE BY THE FLOWERS OF SEXUALLY REPRODUCING PLANTS. IT CONTAINS THE MALE GENES NECESSARY FOR PRODUCTION OF SEEDS AND FRUIT.

prey on other small invertebrates, and the giant desert version even consumes small lizards and rodents. In contrast, the giant desert millipede is a gentle herbivore, completely harmless, although it can ooze a foul-tasting chemical to avoid predation.

Scorpions eat other small invertebrates, including other scorpions. Bark scorpions (*Centruroides exilicauda*) are small, yellowish, and have a highly venomous sting. Striped tail or devil's scorpions (*Vaejovis spinigerus*) are far less venomous, having a sting comparable to that of bees. They are brownish with dark longitudinal ridges underneath the tail. The giant hairy scorpion (*Hadrurus arizonensis*) looks frightening, but is both docile and carries only mild venom. All three species are common in the reserve.

Pollinators in the Pinacate are busy day and night. During the day, bees pollinate ocotillo, agaves, palo verde, most cacti, and many wildflowers—both solitary carpenter bees (*Xylocopa* spp.) and social species like the honeybees (*Apis mellifera*). Between May and September many migratory butterflies, also important pollinators, make an appearance as they wing toward their destinations. Among the migrants most commonly seen are the cloudless sulfur (*Phoebis sennae*), Mexican yellow (*Eurema mexicanum*), tailed orange (*Eurema proterpia*), American snout (*Libytheana carinenta*), and painted lady (*Vanessa cardui*).

At sunset the bees and butterflies bed down, and a nightshift comes out. Night-flying sphinx moths (*Hyles lineata*) pollinate night-blooming cereus

(*Peniocereus greggii*); hawk moths (*Manduca sexta*) pollinate datura (*Datura wrightii*); and the highly specialized senita moths (*Upiga virescens)* and yucca moths (*Tegeticula* sp. and *Parategeticula* sp.) pollinate yucca *(Yucca* sp.*)* and senita.

Aquatic insects take advantage of the few shallow freshwater habitats in or adjacent to the reserve. There is a short stretch of perennial-water in the Río Sonoyta west of the town of Sonoyta; Quitobaquito Spring persists in southern Organ Pipe Cactus National Monument, about 300 feet (91 m) north of the international border and the reserve; several dozen tinajas dot the volcanic field; and a few small artesian springs surface along the shoreline of Adair Bay. All host a plethora of insects during parts of their larval, juvenile and/or adult life cycle, especially dragonflies and water scavenger beetles.[95]

Fish

The Río Sonoyta's feeble headwaters straddle the border east of Sonoyta. The riverbed is now dry along the eastern flank of the Pinacate, but upriver a few perennial-water flow segments sustain aquatic life.[96] The native fishes here are the endangered Sonoyta pupfish (*Cyprinodon eremus*) and longfin dace (*Agosia chrysogaster*). Introduced species include the black catfish (*Ameiurus melas*) and western mosquitofish (*Gambusia affinis*).

THE SONOYTA PUPFISH, AND ITS CLOSE RELATIVE THE DESERT PUPFISH, REACH LENGTHS OF ABOUT 3 INCHES (75 MM). DURING THE SPRING AND SUMMER BREEDING SEASON, MALES TURN A BEAUTIFUL, IRIDESCENT BLUE AND AGGRESSIVELY DEFEND THEIR TERRITORIES FROM OTHER MALES. FEMALES AND NONBREEDING MALES ARE A DRAB WHITISH-TAN WITH DARK VERTICAL BARS. PHYSIOLOGICALLY TOLERANT, THESE FISHES CAN LIVE IN BOTH FRESHWATER AND IN SALINE WATER THAT EXCEEDS THE SALT CONTENT OF SEAWATER.[97]

MANY OF THE REPTILES IN THE PINACATE ARE SIGNIFICANTLY DARKER THAN RELATIVES LIVING ELSEWHERE IN THE SONORAN DESERT. [THESE] DARKER TONES SUGGEST A TREND OF NATURAL SELECTION FOR DARKER SHADES IN SPECIES INHABITING LAVA FLOWS, DARK DESERT PAVEMENT AND CINDER FLATS. THE DARK COLOR MAKES THE ANIMALS LESS CONSPICUOUS TO PREDATORS AND ALSO ENABLES RAPID ABSORPTION OF SOLAR WARMTH, REDUCING THE THERMAL WINDOW FOR SUMMER ACTIVITY, BUT EXTENDING ACTIVITY AT OTHER TIMES OF THE YEAR.[98]

Amphibians and Reptiles

The reserve hosts 4 amphibian and 44 reptile species. Among the more notable are the Sonoran green toad *(Bufo retiformis)*, Gila monster (*Heloderma suspectum*), flat-tailed horned lizard (*Phrynosoma mcallii*), desert iguana (*Dipsosaurus dorsalis*), chuckwalla (*Sauromalus obesus*), desert tortoise (*Gopherus agassizii*), rosy boa (*Lichanura trivirgata*), speckled rattlesnake (*Crotalus mitchelli*) and coral snake (*Micruroides euryxanthus*). In the Gran Desierto, the sidewinder (*Crotalus cerastes*) rules.

Birds

More than 237 species have been recorded in the region, but many are transients from the coastal Adair Bay and Puerto Peñasco.[99] Ornithologists have recorded about 100 resident species,[100] including the rare and/or endangered prairie falcon (*Falco mexicanus*), peregrine falcon (*Falco peregrinus*), ferruginous hawk (*Buteo regalis*), golden eagle (*Aquila chrysaetos*), and ferruginous pygmy-owl (*Glaucidum brasilianum*).[101]

FLAT-TAILED HORNED LIZARD.
Jim Rorabaugh

SONORAN GREEN TOAD.
Arizona-Sonora Desert Museum

SIDEWINDER AT MOON CRATER. Francis M. Harty

SPECKLED RATTLESNAKE. Jim Rorabaugh

DESERT IGUANA WITH SPHINX MOTH. Jim Rorabaugh

ROSY BOA. Arizona-Sonora Desert Museum

CHUCKWALLA AT CERRO COLORADO. Francis M. Harty

OCOTILLO. Bill Glass

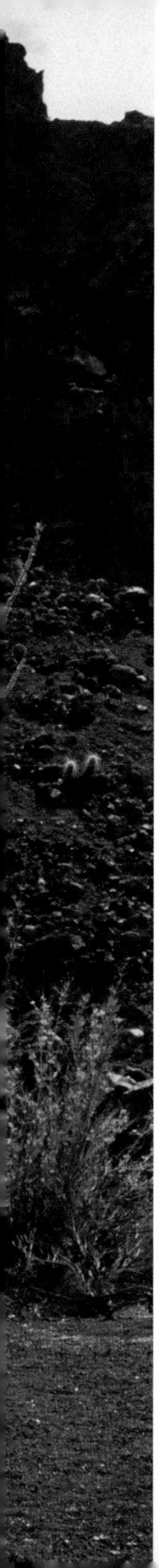

During spring migrations, avian diversity peaks in the Pinacate. On March 16, 2006, the authors watched brilliantly colored hooded (*Icterus cucullatus*), Bullock's (*I. bullockii*), and Scott's (*I. parisorum*) orioles, all feeding on the same ocotillo at El Tecolote campground. Nearby were several species of flycatchers, warblers, and hummingbirds. Overhead a conspicuous parade of turkey vultures (*Cathartes aura*) moved steadily northward. Add to this the many permanent residents, and it is clear why the Pinacate is so special for birdwatchers.

Of the many avian residents, common species include: the red-tailed hawk (*Buteo jamaicaensis),* American kestrel (*Falco sparverius),* greater roadrunner (*Geococcyx californianus),* great horned owl (*Bubo virginianus),* Chihuahuan raven (*Corvus cryptoleucus),* cactus wren (*Campylorhynchus brunneicapillus),* northern mockingbird (*Mimus polyglottos),* black-tailed gnatcatcher (*Polioptila melanura),* phainopepla (*Phainopepla nitens),* and black-throated sparrow (*Amphispiza bilineata).*

A common pollinator here is the rufous hummingbird (*Selasphorus rufus*), which migrates from north-central Mexico in the spring, following the flowering nectar plants. Most rufous hummingbirds spend the summer in the western United States and Canada, but some eventually migrate all the way to Alaska—the longest migration (measured in body-length equivalents) of any bird in the world. Its nectar sources include ocotillo, jícama (*Ipomoea bracteata*), desert honeysuckle (*Anisacanthus thurberi*), limita (*Anisacanthus andersonii*), and Mexican ebony or palo chino (*Havardia mexicana*). Hummingbirds are called *chuparosas* in rural Sonora, and *colibries* in urban areas.

THE PRIMARY BLOOMING SEASON OF THE OCOTILLO COINCIDES WITH THE NORTHERN MIGRATION OF HUMMINGBIRDS IN THE SPRING. THE HUMMINGBIRDS POLLINATE THE BRIGHT RED FLOWERS AND, IN TURN, THE OCOTILLO'S NECTAR AND POLLEN PROVIDE FUEL FOR THEIR MIGRATION.[102]

Some of the reserve's prominent mammals include: bighorn sheep (*Ovis canadensis mexicana*), the endangered Sonoran pronghorn (*Antilocapra americana sonoriensis*), desert mule deer (*Odocoileus hemionus*), white-tailed deer (*Odocoileus virginianus*), javelina (*Tayassu tajacu*), coyote (*Canis latrans*), bobcat (*Lynx rufus*), and mountain lion (*Puma concolor*).[103]

Smaller mammals here include a remarkable diversity of bats, which make their homes in lava tubes and rocky fissures. Species include: the California leaf-nosed bat (*Macrotus californicus*), lesser long-nosed bat (*Leptonycteris yerbabuenae)*, pallid bat (*Antrozous pallidus*), big brown bat (*Eptesicus fuscus*), California myotis (*Myotis californicus*), western pipistrelle (*Pipistrellus hesperus*), and Brazilian free-tailed bat (*Tadarida brasiliensis*), also called the Mexican free-tailed bat. One lava cave in the Ives Flow is estimated to host a maternity colony of 100,000 lesser long-nosed bats.[104] At night, bats pollinate yuccas and columnar cacti, such as the saguaro and organ pipe.

SONORAN PRONGHORN. Jim Hedrick

PALLID BAT. Paul and Shirley Berquist, Arizona-Sonora Desert Museum

DESERT BIGHORN RAM. Bob Sharp

ONE LAVA CAVE IN THE IVES FLOW IS ESTIMATED TO HAVE A MATERNITY COLONY OF 100,000 LESSER LONG-NOSED BATS. BECAUSE ONLY ADULT FEMALES MIGRATE NORTH, THERE ARE NO ADULT MALES OF THIS SPECIES ON THE RESERVE. THE BIRTH OF THE YOUNG COINCIDES WITH THE RIPENING OF SAGUARO CACTUS FRUITS, WHICH ARE THE BAT MOTHER'S ENERGY SOURCE FOR FEEDING THEIR YOUNG.

BABY LESSER LONG-NOSED BAT. Richard C. Brusca

HUMAN HISTORY

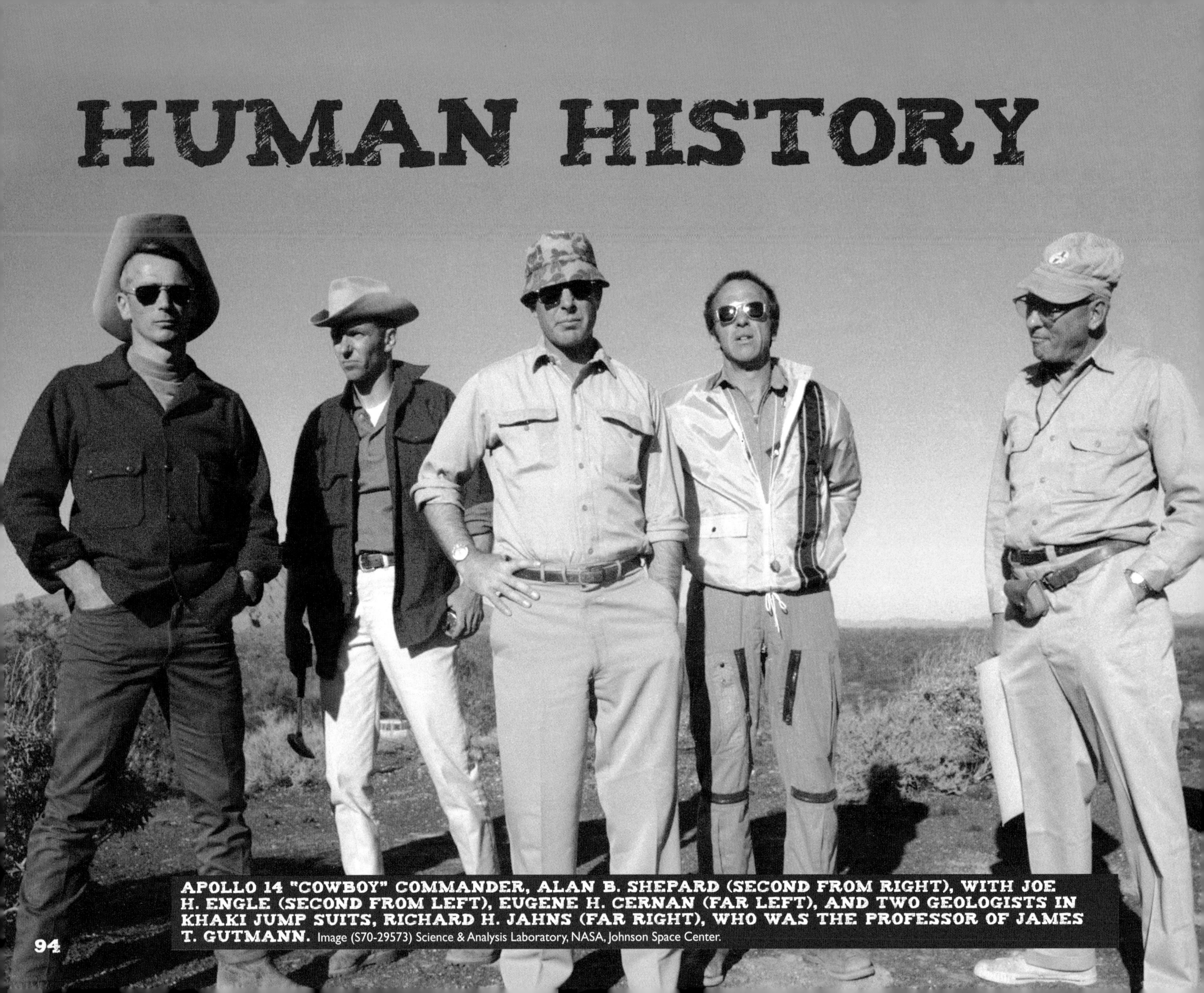

APOLLO 14 "COWBOY" COMMANDER, ALAN B. SHEPARD (SECOND FROM RIGHT), WITH JOE H. ENGLE (SECOND FROM LEFT), EUGENE H. CERNAN (FAR LEFT), AND TWO GEOLOGISTS IN KHAKI JUMP SUITS, RICHARD H. JAHNS (FAR RIGHT), WHO WAS THE PROFESSOR OF JAMES T. GUTMANN. Image (S70-29573) Science & Analysis Laboratory, NASA, Johnson Space Center.

The Devil's Highway

Native peoples and early European travelers followed two main routes from northern Sonora to the Yuma Crossing of the Colorado River, and onward to California. One of these ancient routes is the Devil's Highway (*El Camino del Diablo*), undoubtedly named for its heat, lack of water, and other sources of tribulation. The route began in Altar or Caborca, Sonora, headed northwestward to the Río Sonoyta, and continued on to Quitobaquito Spring. It then turned back to the Río Sonoyta then northward into what is now Cabeza Prieta National Wildlife Refuge in the United States. Finally, the route ran westward across the northernmost edge of the Pinacate lava field, passing unpredictable water sources, including Tinajas Altas, before reaching the Gila River east of Yuma.

The Devil's Highway was used as a Native American travel and trade route long before explorers from the Old World arrived. In 1540, the ill-fated Spanish explorer Melchior Díaz, detached from the Vásquez de Coronado Expedition, probably used part of this route to get to the Yuma Crossing. We know that Father Eusebio Francisco Kino in the 1690s and early 1700s and Juan Bautista de Anza in 1774 and 1776, among others in the eighteenth century, used this route, as did many of the "forty-niners" during the nineteenth-century California gold rush. In the 1860s, when gold was discovered along the lower Colorado River, a new wave of travelers could have coined the name *El Camino del Diablo*. However, the actual source of this name remains a mystery.[105]

WORN INTO THE GRANITE OF A STEEP, RUGGED CANYON, NINE NATURAL WATER TANKS—THE TINAJAS ALTAS—LIE IN THE EAST SIDE OF THE TINAJAS ALTAS MOUNTAINS ALONG THE WESTERN STRETCH OF THE DEVIL'S HIGHWAY. THE NAME TRANSLATES TO HIGH *(ALTAS)* WATER TANKS *(TINAJAS)*.

QUITOBAQUITO MAY DERIVE ITS NAME FROM THE SPANISH *QUITOVAC*, AN O'ODHAM SETTLEMENT SOUTHEAST OF SONOYTA. THE HIA C'ED O'ODHAM CALL QUITOBAQUITO *'A'AL VAIPIA*, MEANING "LITTLE SPRING" OR "LITTLE WATER."[108]

QUITOBAQUITO POND. Organ Pipe Cactus National Monument

Some undocumented legends from the early 1850s tell of a fabled Californian outlaw called Zorro (fox in Spanish), who brought stolen horses along the Devil's Highway and sold them in Sonora. The legend is reputedly based on the outlaw Joaquín Murrieta. Fact or myth, Zorro may represent a composite of several real or imaginary bandits, and one or more may have used this route.

The Hia C'ed O'odham, familiar with the trail and the elusive water holes, often guided European travelers. However, travel on this route virtually stopped when the Southern Pacific Railroad reached Yuma in 1877 and points farther east in 1880. It was, and still is, treacherous.[106] At the beginning of the twentieth century, some 400 human graves, countless carcasses of livestock, and rock configurations were recorded along its length.

Yuma lies at the historic junction of the Colorado and Gila Rivers. When the Spanish first arrived in this area, they observed myriad smoke plumes from Native fires that blanketed the valley. The Spanish word for smoke is *humo*, and in time this word apparently evolved into "Yuma."[107] At a point called the Yuma Crossing two small granite hills rise above the surrounding floodplain. It is the only spot where

CABEZA PRIETA NATIONAL WILDLIFE REFUGE TAKES ITS NAME FROM A WHITE GRANITE MOUNTAIN CAPPED BY BLACK BASALT IN THE WESTERN PART OF THE REFUGE. THE NAME TRANSLATES TO "DARK HEAD" (*PRIETA* MEANS "DARK," *CABEZA*, "HEAD").

LOOKING SOUTH WITH CABEZA PRIETA MOUNTAIN IN FOREGROUND, DEVIL'S HIGHWAY RUNNING THROUGH UPPER MOST (LEFT TO RIGHT) VALLEY, AND PINACATE AT TOP ON HORIZON. Photo by Peter L. Kresan

THREE INTERPRETATIONS HAVE BEEN SUGGESTED FOR THE NAME DERIVATION OF THE TOWN OF AJO. THE FIRST POINTS TO THE AJO LILY *(HESPEROCALLIS UNDULATA)*, WHICH HAS LARGE WHITE FLOWERS AND A BULBOUS ROOT THAT LOOKS LIKE GARLIC—*AJO* IN SPANISH. THE SECOND REFERENCES THE SMALL NATIVE ONION *(ALLIUM MACROPETALUM)*, WHICH HAS A GARLICLIKE FLAVOR. A THIRD MAKES THE CASE FOR ITS DERIVATION FROM THE O'ODHAM WORD *AU'AUHO*—A PIGMENT THEY USED FOR FACE PAINT THAT THEY OBTAINED FROM COPPER-RICH MINERALS IN THE AJO AREA.[109]

AJO LILY. Francis M. Harty

early travelers could easily cross the lower Colorado River. It is also the site where the first southern railroad and first southern highway in the United States crossed into California.

A second route from northern Sonora to California went north to the Santa Cruz River in northern Sonora, just southeast of the current U.S.-Mexico border at Nogales. Travelers followed the Santa Cruz River, which had predictable water for much of its length as far as Tucson. The route then continued northward, with no guarantee of surface water, to the Gila River southwest of Phoenix, then westward along the abundant flow of the Gila to Yuma.

Both routes had advantages and disadvantages, and early travelers had to choose. The Devil's Highway was shorter by about 150 miles, but water sources were scarce or unreliable. The Santa Cruz route was longer and much more prone to Apache attacks, but offered predictable surface water. Many took a chance on the shortcut.

Native Americans

When Europeans arrived in the 1500s and 1600s to what are now the Arizona-Sonora borderlands, people who spoke an O'odham language had long made the region their home. They called themselves Hia C'ed O'odham. In the O'odham language, *hitata* means "sand," *c'ed* means "in," and *O'odham* means "people." Others called these people Sand Papago, *Pinacateños, or Areneños* (people of the sand). The Hia C'ed ranged from the gulf on the west to Ajo on the east, the Gila River on the north, and south into northwestern Sonora, including the Pinacate.

Exactly when humans arrived in the Pinacate area is still uncertain. Until recently, the most popular school of thought had them arriving 13,100 to 12,900 years ago as members of the Clovis Culture, a view based on numerous carbon-14 dates taken from hunting sites in the Southwest.[110] The few large, distinctive spear points that have been found suggest that at this time, when the region was cooler and wetter, native people hunted large game such as mammoth, bison, and (yes) camel.[111]

A second school of thought held by some archaeologists, including Julian Hayden (who did the only extensive archaeological research in the Pinacate) proposes that humans arrived thousands of years earlier.[112] Hayden calls these earliest peoples *Malpais*,

MALPAIS STONE TOOL INBEDDED IN DESERT PAVEMENT.
Julian Hayden, courtesy Stephen Hayden

SLEEPING CIRCLE.
Francis M. Harty

EARLY SAN DIEGUITO TOOLS.
Julian Hayden, courtesy Stephen Hayden

distinguishing them from the later San Dieguito culture on the basis of an array of stone tools more heavily coated with desert varnish than San Dieguito tools. These artifacts are frequently found imbedded as part of the older desert pavements, and equally heavily varnished, rather than on top of the pavement or imbedded in younger pavements with distinctly lighter varnish. Carbon-14 ages tens of thousands of years old were obtained from seashells found in human middens in sand dunes of the Gran Desierto bordering Adair Bay, suggesting very early human occupation.[113] Some archaeologists have questioned relating the dates on these seashells to human presence,[114] but critics of this evidence have yet to explain how shells can be deposited on top of sand dunes in such quantity, except by man.[115] The debate continues.

The San Dieguito Culture came to inhabit the area between 10,250 and 8,450 years ago. Primarily centered in the lower Colorado River Valley, this culture extended from the southern California coast to the San Pedro River Valley in southeastern Arizona, and from northwestern Mexico to the eastern Great Basin. In the Pinacate, San Dieguito people left trails, petroglyphs, rock cairns along trails, clearings surrounded by rocks usually interpreted as "sleeping circles," and simple stone tools.[116]

Between 8,000 and 5,000 years ago, during an interval known as the Altithermal, the climate of the region was much warmer and drier than today. Humans and many larger animals apparently moved out of the area at that time, returning only when living conditions improved.[117]

Some 5,000 years ago, people of the Amargosa Culture (also called Desert or Archaic Culture by some archaeologists) settled in the region. These presumably Uto-Aztecan-speaking people may be the ancestors of the Hia C'ed O'odham.[118] The Amargosans used smaller spear points to hunt small game, and seasonally exploited marine

GYRATORY CRUSHERS. Julian Hayden, courtesy Stephen Hayden

MARIA RUIZ USING GYRATORY CRUSHER. Julian Hayden, courtesy Stephen Hayden

fishes and shellfish along the shores of the upper gulf.[119] Gradually these peoples began to harvest and process native foodplants such as mesquite pods and grass seeds, a practice known because of the deep grinding (mortar) holes still seen in volcanic bedrock outcrops throughout the area. They used an unusual type of mortar, a gyratory crusher, made of basalt with a hole perforated in its bottom.[120]

Like the Malpais and San Dieguitos before them, the Amargosans had campsites but no permanent dwellings. They left behind stone tools, bedrock and portable metates and mortars, rock shelters, trails, trail shrines, "sleeping circles," and giant zoomorphic figures of animals and humans known as "intaglios" or "geoglyphs" on prepared ground.[121] Shell middens containing stone tools from a preceramic culture show evidence of their presence on the coast south of the Pinacate.

Scientists dated a wooden atlatl (a spear-throwing device) found in a lava-tube cave in the Pinacate at about 3,450 years old, documenting a change in hunting technology.[122]

MORTAR HOLE AT TINAJA DE LOS PAPAGOS.
Larry Marshall

At Tinaja Romero, on the southeast side of the Pinacate, Hohokam-style petroglyphs depicting shells appeared sometime between 1,450 and 550 years ago. These petroglyphs suggest that Hohokam (now spelled *Huhugam* by the O'odham) from along the Santa Cruz River Valley, near present-day Tucson, conducted treks by way of the Pinacate for salt and seashells along the upper gulf.[123]

Natives of the Pinacate region did not make pottery, but obtained it through trade with Yuma peoples along the lower Colorado River. Based on the presence of various Yuma pottery there, this trading took place between 1,300 and 500 years ago.[124]

By 1,300 years ago, native peoples of the area reportedly developed a tradition of cremating bighorn sheep, although the motivation behind this is not clear.[125] Practices in dealing with the dead varied among these prehistoric cultures. The Hohokam and Yumas primarily practiced cremation, while other cultures buried their dead.[126]

From the earliest hunters to the historical Hia C'ed, the region's peoples depended on gathering plants,

POSSIBLE HOHOKAM PETROGLYPHS AT TINAJA ROMERO. Julian Hayden, courtesy Stephen Hayden

THE *LOS VIDRIOS* SITE, JUST EAST OF THE VOLCANIC FIELD ALONG THE RÍO SONOYTA, WAS A LOCAL SOURCE OF OBSIDIAN (VOLCANIC GLASS) FOR TOOLS AND PROJECTILE POINTS. THIS SITE CONTAINS OBSIDIAN-RICH VOLCANIC DOMES APPROXIMATELY 30-MILLION YEARS OLD.[130]

hunting, and collecting resources from the gulf to survive. Indigenous peoples' survival depended on knowledge of the location of animals to hunt, productive coastal sites for gathering seafoods, and availability of plant foods at all seasons. They ate plants fresh or cooked, and dried foods for future consumption. Dune or sand root, an underground tuber high in carbohydrates, was a staple food.[127]

Sometime before the arrival of the first Spanish explorers, native people began primitive farming practices in a few locations where water was permanently available, such as Quitobaquito Spring and along the Río Sonoyta. The staple cultivated crops, called the "three sisters," were corn, squash, and beans, which the O'odham call *huñ* (corn), *ha:l* (squash), and *bawi* (tepary beans). Dogs were apparently the only animals domesticated by native peoples in the region.[128]

At the Pinacate, volcanic rocks provided the resources for early humans to process plant foods, caves for shelter, and tinaja water sources.[129] Knowing the location of water was critical for survival, and tinajas were at the hub of life. A network of foot trails connected these bedrock water tanks; some can still be seen as narrow, cleared paths on desert pavement. Upland areas in the reserve provided game animals, trees, and a myriad of food plants.

These desert peoples did not build permanent villages because they traveled almost constantly in search of food and water. Evidence of their campsites, often near tinajas, can still be seen as rock circles—which may be all that remains of their temporary dwellings. Though largely undeciphered, petroglyphs and occasional pictographs (paintings on rock surfaces), allow a glimpse into the beliefs and lives of these hardy desert dwellers.

As Europeans moved into the region, the land and resources available to the Hia C'ed became increasingly restricted. Between 1850 and 1851, those called Pinacateños were nearly wiped out by a yellow fever epidemic. Some survivors joined family groups along the Gila River to the north.[131] In 1890, most remaining Pinacateños were murdered by a group of Mexican vigilantes from Sonoyta, ostensibly for repeated attacks on travelers along the Devil's Highway.[132] Juan Caravajales, the last Hia C'ed to reside in the Pinacate area, left to live on the Gila River in 1910.[133]

After Juan Caravajales left, O'odham visited the Pinacate only to perform sacred ceremonies, or as a stop enroute to collect salt and seashells along the upper gulf. Between 1909 and 1910, an O'odham shaman named Queléle accompanied Norwegian explorer Carl Lumholtz to the Pinacate. Queléle used this opportunity to show I'itoi's Cave to young O'odham in the party. The fact that these young O'odham were seeing this place for the first time suggests that knowledge of, and visits to, such sacred sites was by then rapidly disappearing from O'odham cultural traditions.

Today, a thousand or so Hia C'ed live in communities in southwestern Arizona. They do not have a designated reservation, but recently took a step toward reclaiming their homeland by acquiring a piece of ancestral territory near the town of Ajo. In addition to the Hia C'ed, there are two other groups of O'odham: the Tohono (meaning "desert") O'odham, in the area between Ajo and Tucson and in adjacent Sonora, Mexico; and the Akimel (meaning "river" or, literally, "oh look, it is running") O'odham near Phoenix. These latter two O'odham groups refer to themselves collectively as *Wa:k* (meaning

O'ODHAM TODAY ALSO CALL THE SAGUARO CACTUS "O'ODHAM" BECAUSE OF THE BELIEF THAT THEY ARE REINCARNATED AS SAGUAROS, WHICH OFTEN GIVE THE ILLUSION OF A HUMAN SHAPE, AS SUGGESTED IN THE PHRASE "ARMS OF A SAGUARO."

O'ODHAM CREATION STORIES ARE PASSED DOWN BY ORAL HISTORIES THROUGH GENERATIONS OF INDIVIDUALS OR FAMILY GROUPS. THE STORIES THAT SURVIVE HAVE BEEN FILTERED BY TIME AND BY TELLERS ALONG THE WAY. IT IS TRADITIONAL PRACTICE THAT STORIES TOLD ARE CREDITED TO THE SPECIFIC INDIVIDUALS FROM WHOM THE STORY WAS HEARD. IDENTIFYING THESE INDIVIDUALS IS THE O'ODHAM WAY OF ACKNOWLEDGING THE SOURCE, SOMETHING LIKE OUR ENDNOTE REFERENCES.

"a place where water goes underground") in reference to their historical tie with the intermittent Santa Cruz River, which links their communities.

The first Spaniards in the area called these three O'odham groups *Pimas*, a term still used today. When Spaniards arrived they asked these people their name. The O'odham responded, *pim*. Thinking this was the name they called themselves, the Spanish added an "a" to the end of pim to latinize it, thus coining the word Pima. It was later learned that *pim* means "huh?" or "I do not understand" in their language. The area where these peoples lived was called the *Pimería Alta* (Land of the Upper Pima) on early Spanish maps. Another name the Spaniards called these people was *Papago*, a slang name used by Native neighbors in the area for "bean eater," because the O'odham cultivated a variety of native bean plants.

In O'odham creation stories, the Pinacate is sacred because it is one of their places of origin. According to some legends, the summit of the Sierra Pinacate is the mythological place of their creation. The Hia C'ed call the Sierra Pinacate *Tjuktóak, S-cuk Do'ag, Chuk Toakch or Schuk Toak* (*schuk* means black and *toak,* mountain).[134]

One O'odham story relates that after a great flood, the Elder Brother deity, I'itoi, landed on *Schuk Toak* and created the O'odham people. I'itoi reportedly lived in a cave (created by the roof collapse of a pahoehoe lava-flow tube) on the southeast side of Carnegie Cone.[135] Visiting O'odham left offerings of feathers, plants, and revered objects at this sacred cave. The Tohono O'odham honor another I'itoi's Cave on the west side of a high peak to the southwest of Tucson. O'odham call this peak *Waw Giwulik*, meaning "rock drawn in at the middle."[136] The Spaniards called it Baboquivari, the name used on maps today.

According to an O'odham storyteller:

> *After the Great Flood, I'itoi, Elder Brother, searched for a piece of solid land [on which] to rest together with the crow and the coyote. The untiring ants brought earth and rocks up from the depths to please him. Thus arose the sacred mountain of El Pinacate; large craters, lava-rivers, and innumerable cones were also created in the same way. Broad, soft valleys of sand spread out between the volcanoes and lava frozen just yesterday.*[137]

This is an interesting interpretation, given that some anthills and cinder cones are remarkably similar in appearance and structure, though significantly different in size. Both may have similar angles of repose and craters at their summits.

An O'odham legend recorded by Lumholtz suggests that their ancestors may have witnessed volcanic activity.

> *Í'itoi lived in Baboquivari before he came to Pinacate. At that time there were many people in the Pinacate. The mountains were very high then, and the sun used to set soon after it had risen, so the days were very short. He saw that this did not suit the people, and he decided to lower the mountains. He built two fires, where the two peaks are found to-day, making fire by drilling one stick into another one. The wind blew the ashes about to all parts and made the mountains lower, covering the country so as to look as seen today. After that the people lived contented, and there was not so much shade from the west.* [138]

Hartmann speculates that native people *did witness fumaroles*, such as the steam vents in Yellowstone National Park, *or mild eruptive activity in the Pinacate area.*[139] The 12,000 ± 4,000-years-old dating of La Laja Flow and the O'odham legend recorded by Lumholtz both support this possibility. If the legend reflects ancient observations of volcanism, this implies a cultural and informational continuity spanning up to 12,000 years—from the earliest inhabitants to the present day. Alternatively, the legend may arise out of volcanic activity in the more recent past. In that case, geologists have yet to find and date materials from these events. If the activity was only gas or steam expulsions, we may never know if or when this happened, since such events may leave no physical record.

Spaniards

The first Spaniard to set foot in the Pinacate was probably the conquistador Melchior Díaz. He was an officer in the infamous Francisco Vásquez de Coronado Expedition that came north from west-central Mexico in 1540 on a quest for the legendary Seven Golden Cities of Cíbola. Díaz and a detachment of about twenty-five soldiers, with a flock of sheep for food, likely passed along or near the Devil's Highway enroute to the Colorado River Delta, where they hoped to meet supply ships under the command of Captain Hernando de Alarcón, another arm of the Coronado Expedition.[140] Díaz started from the Sonora River Valley near the town of Arizpe. His exact route is unknown, but he likely crossed the Colorado River at present-day Yuma. Alarcón's ships departed before his arrival, and the two parties never met. Díaz then traveled southwest to the geothermal field of mud pots and sulfur springs now known as Cerro Prieto and Volcano Lake, southeast of Mexicali in northern Baja California.

> *Beds of burning lava [horrified the Spaniards]. No one could cross them, as it would be like going into the sea to drown. The ground...resounded like a kettle-drum, as if there were lakes underneath. It was amazing to see the cinders boil in some places, for it looked like something infernal.*[141]

Here, or nearby, Díaz was mortally wounded in an unfortunate self-inflicted mishap. As he galloped on horseback chasing a dog that molested the expedition's sheep, the butt of his own lance stabbed Díaz in the groin. On the twentieth day of the return journey, he died, presumably succumbing to infection. Some historians believe Díaz was buried in or near the northern part of the Pinacate, although the precise location of his grave is not known.[142] The returning expedition reported the area contained nothing of worth, and Spaniards did not return for another 160 years.[143] On subsequent maps, it was labeled a no-man's-land (*terra mala*) or rough country (*mal pais*) to denote the volcanic landscape.

In 1687, father Eusebio Francisco Kino, a 42-year-old priest from Segno, Italy, arrived in the Pimería Alta. Kino spent the remaining twenty-four years of his life in the Pimería Alta to Christianize, explore, and map the *so sadly watered vineyard of the Lord.*[144] He was a member of the Jesuit Order (Society of Jesus or Black Robes), founded by Saint Ignatius Loyola in 1534. The first overseas missionary of the Jesuit Order was Saint Francis Xavier, with whom Kino was so enamored that he changed his middle name to Francisco. His mission near Tucson was named San Xavier del Bac.[145] However, Kino was not only a missionary but a geographer who made good use of his survey tools, including a compass, sextant, and telescope.[146]

Kino visited the Pinacate three times between 1698 and 1706. He climbed the highest peak in 1698, and in 1701 named it Cerro de Santa Clara in honor of Sister Clare of Assisi, who founded the Poor Clare Order (also called the Poor Ladies) in 1212. Sister Clare was a close friend of Saint Francis of Assisi, who founded the Franciscan Order (Friars Minor or Brown Robes) in 1209. Kino and his sometime companions, Juan Mateo Manje (a soldier) and Juan María Salvatierra (another Jesuit priest), correctly recognized that the Sierra Pinacate was of volcanic origin.[147]

One of the most influential individuals during the early colonial period of the Sonoran Desert, Kino introduced cattle, horses, goats, sheep, and wheat—a winter crop that "became so important to the Pimas along the Gila River that some even began to call the first month of the year 'Wheat Harvest Moon' instead of 'Saguaro Harvest Moon'."[148] (The traditional O'odham year begins in June, with the summer solstice and ripening of saguaro fruit.)

Hartmann[149] and Pinacate historian Ronald Ives[150] describe the three trips (1698, 1702, 1706) Kino made to the Pinacate in search of a land passage to California. In 1706, from Santa Clara peak, Kino correctly observed that Baja California was a peninsula and not an island, as some early navigators had erroneously reported and some of his contemporaries still believed. Two of Kino's travel companions expressed their impression of the area.

> *It gave us more horror to discover...a great chain of mountains, which seem also to be made of cinders, so that I do not know where there is a place in which*

THE PORT AND TOWN SOUTH OF THE PINACATE has several names. Lieutenant Robert Hardy named a coastal basalt hill Rocky Point at a time when there were no permanent inhabitants living there (although the presence of numerous nearby shell middens confirms that the O'odham and their ancestors seasonally visited this area for thousands of years; they collected salt and seashells, and ate fishes and shellfish). In the early twentieth century, the name changed to Punta Peñasco (Rocky Point). Later, in the 1940s after a sizeable fishing community had formed, the railroad arrived. In the early 1970s the Mexican government dredged an estuary on the north side of the volcanic hill and turned it into a harbor. The site was renamed Puerto (port) Peñasco. Today, Rocky Point and Puerto Peñasco are interchangeably used for the same location, although the latter is the official name recognized in Mexico.

> *can be better shown the face of the earth in the general conflagration before judgment day.*[151]
>
> [From the top of a peak] *we could see a big hole of such depth that it caused terror and fear.*[152]

This is the first written record of a Pinacate maar crater.

Gringos

At the end of the seventeenth century, after the exploration and mapping journeys of Kino, more and more Europeans journeyed into the arid lands of what is now northwest Mexico. Beginning in the 1840s, and especially following the Mexican-American War, these newcomers would be called *gringos*.

Lieutenant Robert William Hale Hardy journeyed by sea to the Colorado River Delta in 1826. Hardy was a sea captain commissioned by the General Pearl and Coral Fishery Association of England to search for pearls and corals in the upper gulf. He named Rocky Point as a landmark, Adair Bay after a friend, and the Hardy River channel in the delta after his family.[153] A passage of Hardy's impression of the area is sobering:

> *A traveler sees many things which give rise to a multitude of feelings...some of them pleasing, some painful, and yet others*

productive of wonder and surprise. My own sensations were of this latter kind.... [This country] is probably in the same state that it was ages ago....those who love the total absence of sound, and of the...'busy hum of men'...would here find a solitude so absolutely melancholy, that they would never willingly again quit the society of their fellow creatures.[154]

John Woodhouse Audubon, son of the famous artist and bird painter John James Audubon, journeyed from central Chihuahua to the Colorado River Delta. He passed by the Pinacate in the late 1840s and made watercolors and sketches of the region. In 1849, Audubon wrote an account of his travels, in which he described an O'odham settlement east of the Pinacate.[156]

Why it is that these Indians settle in such a country, I cannot conceive, for even the lizards, in most places innumerable, are scarce here.

Audubon also recalled an incident during his travels.

We were hooted and shouted at as we passed through, and called 'Gringoes.'

THE BASALT AT ROCKY POINT IS ABOUT 15 MILLION YEARS OLD.[155]

At the end of the Mexican-American War in 1848, the Gila River became the international boundary, leaving the rest of what would later become southern Arizona as part of Mexico. The international border moved southward to its present-day location with the Gadsden Purchase in 1854, subdividing the Sonoran Desert. The motivation for this purchase was to provide a route to connect California with the eastern United States. The 29,640 square miles of land cost ten million dollars, or about 53 cents an acre.

Hartmann captures cultural dynamics in the region at the end of the 1800s:

A reference by John Woodhouse Audubon may be the first recorded English use of the word "gringo." The term appeared in Spanish language dictionaries and literature, and was in daily use, in the eighteenth and mid-nineteenth centuries. Etymologists now generally agree that "gringo" is a corruption of the Spanish griego, meaning "Greek," a term used for foreigners who spoke Spanish badly or with a strong accent so as to "speak Greek." Other interpretations—that the term originated during the Mexican-American War or derived from the singing of "Green Grow the Rushes, O"—has been discredited, but certainly makes for a good campfire story. Until recent decades, the term was usually used as an ethnic slur, especially toward American and other English-speaking peoples in the context of cultural and political meddling in Latin America. But today, "gringo" is often used in a friendlier manner, much the same as an American is called a "Yank" by Australians or Canadians.[157]

Three Americans, Tom Childs, Rube Daniels and John Merrill, married three Papago sisters and settled at Quitobaquito.... According to local gossip in 1932, Childs...had married a Papago to learn the secret location of gold that had supposedly been stolen by Indians from the old Sonoyta mission many years before.[158]

There was no gold cache. Moreover, the women were not from the area, and their own people would not have known about the gold rumors. Childs stayed married to his wife until her death.[159]

The Great Expeditions

Many current place names in the Pinacate area derive from writer-scientists of the early 1900s who thought they were the first to discover such a peculiar landscape. Hartmann identified this period as the time of the "Great Expeditions."[160]

William Hornaday of New York, who believed "no American has set a foot in the area, nor mapped the mysteries of the Pinacates," led the most famous expedition.[161] In 1907 the Hornaday Expedition collected plants and animals, and photographed, described, and produced the first reliable map of the area.[162] For some on the expedition it was an opportunity to hunt. According to Godfrey Sykes, the geographer on the expedition:

TUMAMOC HILL TAKES ITS NAME FROM THE O'ODHAM WORD FOR HORNED LIZARD.

> *Our guest of honor was the late Dr. Hornaday, Director for many years of the New York Zoological Park and a big-game hunter of note. He was accompanied by another big-game enthusiast, John M. Phillips of Pittsburgh, Pa., and their quest was the Big Horn Mountain sheep,... heads of rams were obtained which were declared to be remarkable for the size and symmetry of the horns, and a region which had not hitherto been subjected to scientific scrutiny had been pretty thoroughly...examined.... [And with] steaks cut from the hindquarters of one of the luckless rams, and flanked by the inevitable frijoles, one could hardly wish for more satisfactory filling after a day of strenuous scrambling over the scenery.*[163]

Members of the Hornaday Expedition named Carnegie Peak in honor of the Carnegie Institution and Pittsburgh industrialist-philanthropist Andrew Carnegie. Carnegie was a principal benefactor of the Desert Botanical Laboratory on Tumamoc Hill in Tucson, Arizona, where the expedition originated.[164] Hornaday also assigned the scientific name for the saguaro cactus, *Carnegiea gigantea,* in honor of Carnegie and the Carnegie Institution.

Carl Lumholtz, a Norwegian explorer and ethnographer, conducted a small expedition of the Pinacate and Gran Desierto in 1909 and 1910, during the early stages of the Mexican Revolution. The young wagon driver and guide for Lumholtz was Alberto Celaya of Sonoyta, for whom Celaya Crater was named. This trip resulted in Lumholtz's classic book *New Trails in Mexico,* which gives tribute to the Hia C'ed O'odham and their historical ties to the Pinacate.[165]

Early twentieth-century expeditions like these provided a better understanding of the landscape and the region's natural resources. Documents from these expeditions show that during the last 450 years perceptions of the Pinacate changed from a *sacred place* and home of the O'odham's Elder Brother, I'itoi, to a place that caused *terror and fear* for Spanish missionaries, to a *magnificent, grand Vesuvius in the desert* for later explorers and scientists.[166]

Apollo Astronauts

During the great space race of the mid-twentieth century, thirty astronauts of the U.S. National Aeronautics and Space Administration (NASA) undertook geological training in the Pinacate to prepare for collecting moon rocks during Apollo missions.[167] They trained here in November and December of 1965 and '66, March 1967, and February 1970.[168] On the northeast rim of Molina Crater a large volcanic boulder commemorates the astronauts' last official visit, with *APOLLO 14 NASA 2/16/70* scratched into its rock varnish.

Ejidos

Beginning in late 1969, *ejidos*, a legal form of communal land tenure, were established by the Mexican government in the Pinacate. The people who communally own the land are called *ejidatarios* (ejido members). As of the year 2000, there were 28 ejidos wholly or partially contained in the Pinacate reserve. About 200 people lived there permanently, and an estimated 1,288 people had legal rights to use part of the land. Most ejidatarios were located along National Highways 2 and 8, and in the semi-urban communities of Puerto Peñasco, Sonoyta, and San Luis del Río Colorado adjacent to the reserve. Originally, they expected to make a living using agricultural technology and ranching operations, but most soon realized that the land was not what they had hoped it would be. When they began to migrate back to urban centers, much of the land lay unattended and it quickly became susceptible to unregulated practices such as illegal hunting, cactus poaching, cinder mining, wood harvesting, overgrazing, and recreation in its negative aspects. After the reserve was established in 1993, livestock was removed.[169] Today, the remaining ejidatarios maintain rights to their land, but gain little from it.

Evidence of failed attempts at agriculture, such as abandoned irrigation constructs and fallow fields, can be seen just west of the reserve's biological field station, off the dirt road leading to the Red Cone and El Tecolote campgrounds. Such failures were caused by the difficulty of finding a reliable water table, high expenses for electricity to pump the ground water, lack of organization and infrastructure of the ejido communities, and increasing soil salinity due to rapid evaporation of irrigation water. In effect, the soil soon became too salty to grow crops.

APOLLO ROCK, NE RIM OF MOLINA CRATER. READS 'APOLLO 14 NASA 2 16 70'.
Francis M. Harty

THE FIRST FOUR OF 28 EJIDOS in the Pinacate reserve, were created on September 24, 1969—ejidos Cerro Colorado, Jaime Jeréz, Josefa Ortíz de Domínguez, and Punta Peñasco. The other 24 ejidos were created in the 1970s and include: 5 de Mayo, Aquiles Serdán, Aquiles Serdán 1, Aquiles Serdán 2, Aquiles Serdán 3, Aquiles Serdán Bis, Carlos Salinas de Gortari, El Pedregal, El Sinaloense, General de División Joaquín Amaro, General Felipe Angeles, General Vicente Guerrero, Ignacio Zaragoza, La Frontera, Lagos de Moreno, Las Lágrimas, Los Norteños, Morelia, Nueva Creación, Profesor Alfredo López Aceves, Santo Domingo, Sierrita del Rosario, Toboyori Segundo, and Valle del Pinacate.

RANCH INHOLDING ON THE EDGE OF THE GRAN DESIERTO. Organ Pipe Cactus National Monument

EPILOGUE

In the history of this land, the establishment of The Pinacate and Gran Desierto de Altar Biosphere Reserve stands out as a singularly propitious event, one that has already taken this unique landscape a step closer to the veneration once afforded by ancient peoples—promoting the health of the ecological community, affording opportunities for scientific research, and establishing a respectful relationship with the people of northwest Sonora and visitors from around the world. For those who walk its volcanic fields and shifting dunes, the Pinacate instills due awe of the Earth's dynamic forces and reminds us of our place in time. One day, rivers of hot red liquid rock may flow once again in the Pinacate. We close recalling Caroline Wilson's words in her *Reserva de la Biosfera del Pinacate* more than fifteen years ago.

> *In the last 30 years, interest in the Pinacate has escalated and considerable research has been completed on its archaeology, geology and ecology. The unique combination of volcanics, plants and prehistory here is duplicated nowhere else. It draws not only scientists, but also people who simply want to enjoy its beauty, serenity and wilderness.* [170]

Chronology of Natural and Human Events in the Pinacate

YEARS A.D.	
1993	The Pinacate and Gran Desierto de Altar Biosphere Reserve established
1969	First ejidos established
1956	Julian Hayden begins work in Pinacate
1930s	Ronald Ives begins work in Pinacate
1910	Last O'odham resident leaves Pinacate
1909	Carl Lumholtz Expedition
1907	William Hornaday Expedition
1890s	Pinacateños nearly wiped out by Mexican vigilantes from Sonoyta
1854	Gadsden Purchase
1850s	Pinacateño population drastically reduced by yellow fever epidemic
1840s	John Woodhouse Audubon passes by Pinacate
1826	Lieutenant R. W. H. Hardy visits upper gulf
1698	Padre Eusebio Francisco Kino makes first of three visits to Pinacate
1540	Melchior Díaz is first European to pass by Pinacate; Captain Hernando de Alarcón sails to Colorado River Delta

YEARS AGO	
1,300-500	Reputed cremation of large animals; evidence of Yuma-style pottery
1,450-550	Hohokam-style petroglyphs
3,450	First and only record of atlatl spear-throwing device
5,000	Amargosa Culture
8,000-5,000	Altithermal interval; hiatus in human presence
10,250-8,450	San Dieguito Culture
12,000	Possible presence of paleo-Indian hunters; eruption of La Laja Cone
13,000	Eruption of Ives Flow
27,000	Eruption of El Tecolote Cone
32,000	Eruption of Crater Elegante
38,000	Eruption of Carnegie Cone
185,000	Eruption of MacDougal Crater
1.7 - 1.1 million	Age of Pinacate shield volcano
6 to 4 million	Gulf of California begins to open and Baja peninsula moves apart from mainland
1.4 billion	Age of basement rock at Sierra Blanca

Pinacate Contact Information

From USA to Mexico, dial 011-52 before code zone (#)

Comisión Nacional de Areas Naturales Protegidas
Camino al Ajusco No. 200, Delegación Tlalpan
Col. Jardines en la Montaña
C. P. 14210, México, D. F.
Tel. (555) 449-7000
www.conanp.gob.mx
info@conanp.gob.mx

**Comisión Nacional de Areas Naturales Protegidas,
Dirección Regional Noroeste**
Av. Aquiles Serdán No. 180, Int. 10
Esq. Blvd. Rosales, Planta Alta Edif. Correos
Col. Centro, C. P. 83000, Hermosillo, Sonora
Tel. (662) 217-0173, 213-9926
Fax. (662) 213-4254

Reserva de la Biósfera El Pinacate y Gran Desierto de Altar
Carretera 8, km 51, Puerto Peñasco-Sonoyta
Ejido Los Norteños
Puerto Peñasco, Sonora
Tel. (638) 384-9007/08
Fax. (638) 383-5225
pinacate@conanp.gob.mx

Hours of Operation at Field Station

365 days a year
8:00 am to 5:00 pm (spring, summer, and fall)
9:00 am to 5:00 pm (winter)

Rules and Regulations for Reserve Visitors

http://www.semarnat.gob.mx/sonora/zonas_prot_reglamento_visitantes2.html

Campgrounds

The Pinacate reserve has two campgrounds with picnic tables, but no bathroom facilities or running water. There are no trash containers, so campers must carry out their own trash. Fires are permitted only if visitors bring their own wood. Burn wood in an above ground container, and carry out the ashes. Be prepared to adopt the "leave no trace" policy.

In the south, Red Cone (Cono Rojo) campground is named for a profusion of red cinders in an eroded cinder cone that lies on the north side of the campground. The only designated hiking trail in the reserve leads from Red Cone campground to Santa Clara Peak.

In the north, El Tecolote campground is located between Mayo Cone to the north and Tecolote Cone to the south. Mayo Cone is named for Evans Mayo, a former professor of geology at the University of Arizona.

Visitor Center

The new visitor center is located at the southern tip of the Ives Flow on the shores of the Gran Desierto, with the Sierra Pinacate and the rugged Sierra Blanca as a backdrop. The center offers visitors a space to learn about nature in a modern facility with an auditorium, exhibit hall, museum, and library. Solar panels provide energy to run the building, making it environmentally friendly. To get to the center, turn into the entrance from Highway 8 at kilometer 73, then go west eight kilometers on a dirt road.

For information on ecotours to the Pinacate visit www.laruta.org

ACKNOWLEDGMENTS

This publication is the result of collaborative partnerships with colleagues at the Arizona-Sonora Desert Museum, Cabeza Prieta National Wildlife Refuge, Intercultural Center for the Study of Deserts and Oceans (CEDO), Environmental Education Exchange, La Ruta de Sonora, National Aeronautics and Space Administration (NASA), Organ Pipe Cactus National Monument and Biosphere Reserve, Sierra Pinacate and Gran Desierto de Altar Biosphere Reserve, Sonoran Institute, Sonoran Office of Tourism, Tohono Chul Park, Tucson Audubon Society, United States Fish and Wildlife Service, United States Geological Survey, and the Yuma Crossing National Heritage Area.

We extend special thanks to geologist and volcanologist James T. Gutmann, Professor Emeritus of Earth and Environmental Sciences at Wesleyan University, for sharing his knowledge of forty years of geological research in the Pinacate, for helping us to understand the complexities of the area, and for taking time to review the geological descriptions in early drafts of the text. We are indebted for comments, guidance, photos, reviews, and/or support to: Brian Barns, Paul and Shirley Berquist, Peggy and Rick Boyer, John Bridges, Bill Broyles, Richard C. Brusca, José Castelao, David Cole, Paul Dayton, Mark Dimmitt, Monica Durand, Jo Falls, Erin Fernandez, Lloyd Findley (who wishes to also credit Doug Peacock and Barry Spicer), Bill Glass, Floyd Gray, Gayle and William Hartmann, Francis M. Harty, Trica Hawkins, Stephen Hayden, Jim Hedrick, Peter L. Kresan, Peggy Larson, Jonathan Mabry, José Marcos-Iga, Neil Markowitz, Rodrigo A. Medellín, Susan Cummins Miller, Joaquin Murrieta, Matthew Nelson, Ami Pate, José Dávila Paulin, Jim Rorabaugh, John Scheuring, Bob Sharp, Tom Sharp, Hans Tammemagi, Tom Van Devender, Justin Wilkinson, and Caroline Wilson.

We have benefited greatly from the critical eyes of these competent scholars. Any errors are the sole responsibility of the authors.

Space Shuttle images are courtesy of the Image Science & Analysis Laboratory, NASA Johnson Space Center. These images can be found and downloaded on the NASA website at *http://eol.jsc.nasa.gov* using the photo identification with the image.

The maps of the Pinacate Shield Volcano and regional protected areas are courtesy of Ami Pate (Organ Pipe Cactus National Monument and Biosphere Reserve). The topographic map of the biosphere reserve showing the buffer and core zones is reproduced and modified courtesy of José Dávila Paulin.

The book was designed by Rob Ruisinger of The Robidoux Foundation; final text editing by Linda M. Brewer/Bailiwick, Ink. José Marcos-Iga translated the preface from Spanish to English. John Bridges edited early versions of the manuscript.

This publication was made possible by a grant from The Robidoux Foundation to the nonprofit Environmental Education Exchange.

AUTHORS

Larry G. Marshall
Environmental Education Exchange
738 N. 5th Ave., Suite 100
Tucson, Arizona 85705
lgm120547@aol.com

Clark Blake
Geology Department
Western Washington University,
Bellingham, Washington 98225
mcblake@nas.com

REFERENCES CITED &

Altschul, J. H. and Rankin, A. G. (eds). 2008. *Fragile Patterns: The Archaeology of the Western Papaguería*. University of Arizona Press, Tucson.

Anderson, T. H., and Silver, L. T. 2005. The Mojave-Sonora Megashear – field and analytical studies leading to the conception and evolution of the hypothesis. Geological Society of America, Special Paper 393: 1-50.

Audubon, J. W. 1984. *Audubon's Western Journal, 1849-1851*. University of Arizona Press, Tucson (first published 1906, F. H. Hodder, by A. H. Clark Co., Cleveland).

Beveridge, C., Kocurek, G., Ewing, R. C., Lancaster, N., Morthekai, P., Singhvi, A. K., and Mahan, S. A. 2006. Development of spatially diverse and complex dune-field patterns: Gran Desierto Dune Field, Sonora, Mexico. Sedimentology 53: 1391-1409.

Bezy, J. V., Gutmann, J. T., and Haxel, G. B. 2000. *A Guide to the Geology of Organ Pipe Cactus National Monument and the Pinacate Biosphere Reserve*. Arizona Geological Survey, Down-to-Earth Series, No. 9.

Bonillas, Y. S., Jr. 1910. Estudio químico y óptico de una labradorita del Pinacate, Sonora. Instituto Geológico de México. Parergones 3: 427-432.

Bowden, C. 2006. *Inferno*. University of Texas Press, Austin.

Boyer, R. E. 2004. Rains in the Gran Desierto de Altar. CEDO News 10 (2): 30-31.

Broyles, B. 2006. *Sunshot: Peril and Wonder in the Gran Desierto*. University of Arizona Press, Tucson.

Broyles, B. (ed.). 2007a. Science on Desert and Lava: A Pinacate Centennial, Part I. Journal of the Southwest, 49(2): 129-321.

Broyles, B. (ed.). 2007b. Science on Desert and Lava: A Pinacate Centennial, Part II. Journal of the Southwest, 49(3): 323-505.

Broyles, B., Evans, L., Felger, R. S., and Nabhan, G. P. 2007. Our grand desert: a gazetteer for northwestern Sonora, southwestern Arizona, and northeastern Baja California, pp. 581-679. In: *Dry Borders: Great Natural Reserves of the Sonoran Desert* (Felger, R. S., and Broyles, B., eds.). University of Utah Press, Salt Lake City.

Brusca, R. C. 2004. A history of discovery in the northern Gulf of California, pp. 9-24. In: *A Seashore Guide to the Northern Gulf of California* (Brusca, R. C., Kimrey, E., and Moore, W., eds.). Arizona-Sonora Desert Museum, Tucson.

Brusca, R. C., and Bryner, G. C. 2004. A case study of two Mexican biosphere reserves: the Upper Gulf of California and Colorado River Delta and the El Pinacate and Gran Desierto de Altar biosphere reserves, pp. 21-52. In: *Science and Politics in the International Environment* (Harrison, N. E., and Bryner, G. C., eds.), Lanham MD

Búrquez, A. 2001. Between El Vizcaíno and El Pinacate, pp. 185-206. In: *The Gulf of California: A World Apart* (Gil, P. R., Ezcurra, E., and Mellink, E., eds.). Agrupación Sierra Madre, S.C., México, D. F.

Búrquez, A., and Castillo, C. 1994. Reserva de la Biósfera El Pinacate y Gran Desierto de Altar: entorno biológico y social. Estudios Sociales 5: 9-64.

Cochran, C., Dimmitt, M., Lawler, H., Siminski, P., and Thayer, D. 1990. A Pinacate adventure. Sonorensis, Arizona-Sonora Desert Museum 10 (3): 2-13.

Coffman, J. H. 1997. Origin of the word Gringo. Honduras This Week, January 25, 1997, online edition 39, at www.marrder.com/htw/jan97/Editorial.htm.

Damon, P.E., Long, A., and Sigalove, J. J. 1963. Arizona radiocarbon dates IV, Radiocarbon 5: 283-301.

Davis, O. K., Cutler, A. H., Meldahl, K. H., Palacios-Fest, M. R., Schreiber, J. F., Lock, B. E., Williams, L. J., Lancaster, N., Shaw, C. A., and Sinitiere, S. M. 1990a. Quaternary geology of Bahia Adair and the Gran Desierto region. Fieldtrip Guide for Fourth Workshop, International Geological Correlation Programme (IGCP) 252, March 6-9, 1990, Tucson.

Davis, O. K., Cutler, A. H., Meldahl, K. H., Palacios-Fest, M. R., Schreiber, J. F., Lock, B. E., Williams, L. J., Lancaster, N., Shaw, C. A., and Sinitiere, S.

RECOMMENDED READINGS

M. 1990b. Quaternary and environmental geology of the northeastern Gulf of California. In: *Geologic Excursions through the Sonoran Desert Region, Arizona and Sonora* (Gehrels, G. E., and Spencer, J. E., eds.). Arizona Geological Survey Special Paper 7: 136-154.

Dimmitt, M. A. 2000. Flowering plants of the Sonoran Desert, pp. 153-264. In: *A Natural History of the Sonoran Desert* (Phillips, S. J., and Comus, P. W., eds.). Arizona-Sonora Desert Museum Press (Tucson) and University of California Press, Berkeley.

Donnelly, M. F. 1974. Geology of the Sierra del Pinacate volcanic field in northern Sonora, Mexico, and southern Arizona, U.S.A. Ph.D. dissertation, Stanford University.

Echelle, A. A., Carson, E. W., Echelle, A. F., Van Den Bussche, R. A., Dowling, T. E., and Meyer, A. 2005. Historical biogeography of the New-World pupfish genus *Cyprinodon* (Teleostei: Cyprinodontidae). Copeia 2005 (2): 320-339.

Ezcurra, E., Felger, R. S., Russell, A. D., and Equihua, M. 1988. Freshwater islands in a desert sand sea: the hydrology, flora, and phytogeography of the Gran Desierto oases of northwestern Mexico. Desert Plants 9 (2): 35-63.

Ezell, P. H. 1955. The archaeological delineation of a cultural boundary in Papagueria. American Antiquity 20 (4):367-373.

Felger, R. S. 1998. Sonoran sandfood. Drylands Oasis (Tucson) 1 (1&2): 1, 7.

Felger, R. S. 2000. *Flora of the Gran Desierto and Río Colorado of Northwestern Mexico*. University of Arizona Press, Tucson.

Felger, R. S. 2007a. Living resources at the center of the Sonoran Desert, pp. 147-192. In: *Dry Borders: Great Natural Reserves of the Sonoran Desert* (Felger, R. S., and Broyles, B., eds.). University of Utah Press, Salt Lake City.

Felger, R. S. 2007b. A botanist's view of the center of the Universe, pp. 195-201. In: *Dry Borders: Great Natural Reserves of the Sonoran Desert* (Felger, R. S., and Broyles, B., eds.). University of Utah Press, Salt Lake City.

Felger, R. S., and Broyles, B. (eds.). *Dry Borders: Great Natural Reserves of the Sonoran Desert*. University of Utah Press, Salt Lake City.

Felger, R. S., Broyles, B., Wilson, M. F., Nabhan, G. P., and Turner, D. S. 2007. Six grand reserves, one grand desert, pp. 3-26. In: *Dry Borders: Great Natural Reserves of the Sonoran Desert* (Felger, R. S., and Broyles, B., eds.). University of Utah Press, Salt Lake City.

Felger, R. S., Rutman, S., Wilson, M. F., and Mauz, K. 2007. Botanical diversity of southwestern Arizona and northwestern Sonora, pp. 202-271. In: *Dry Borders: Great Natural Reserves of the Sonoran Desert* (Felger, R. S., and Broyles, B., eds.). University of Utah Press, Salt Lake City.

Ferg, A., and Peachey, W. D. 1998. An atlatl from the Sierra Pinacate. Kiva 64 (2): 175-200.

Granger, B. H. 1982. *Will C. Barnes' Arizona Place Names.* University of Arizona Press, Tucson, (first published 1960).

Griffin, D. J. 2007. Birds of Arizona's southwestern borderland, pp. 280-302. In: *Dry Borders: Great Natural Reserves of the Sonoran Desert* (Felger, R. S., and Broyles, B., eds.). University of Utah Press, Salt Lake City.

Gutmann, J. T. 1972. Eruptive history and petrology of Crater Elegante, Sonora, Mexico. Ph.D. dissertation, Stanford University, Stanford, California.

Gutmann, J. T. 1976. Geology of Crater Elegante, Sonora, Mexico. Geological Society of America Bulletin 87: 1718-1729.

Gutmann, J. T. 1977. Textures and genesis of phenocrysts and megacrysts in basaltic lavas from the Pinacate volcanic field. American Journal of Science 277: 833-861.

Gutmann, J. T. 2002. Strombolian and effusive activity as precursors to phreatomagmatism: eruptive sequence at maars of the Pinacate volcanic field, Sonora, Mexico. Journal of Volcanology and Geothermal Research 113: 345-356.

Gutmann, J. T. 2007. Geologic studies in the Pinacate Volcanic Field. Journal of the Southwest 49 (2): 189-243.

Gutmann, J. T., Turrin, B. D., and Dohrenwend, J.C. 2000. Basaltic rocks from the Pinacate volcanics field yield notably young 40Ar/39Ar ages. Transactions of the American Geophysical Union 81(4): 33.

Gutmann, J. T., and Turrin, B. D. 2006. The age of Crater Elegante, a maar in the Pinacate volcanic field, Sonora, Mexico. Geological Society of America, Abstracts with Programs 38 (6): 32.

Hardy, R. W. H. 1977. *Travels in the Interior of Mexico, in 1825, 1826, 1827, and 1828*. Rio Grande Press. Glorieta, New Mexico, (first published 1829, Colburn & Bentley, London).

Hartmann, W. K. 1989. *Desert Heart: Chronicles of the Sonoran Desert*. Fisher Books, Tucson, Arizona.

Hayden, J. D. 1967. A summary prehistory and history of the Sierra Pinacate, Sonora. American Antiquity 32 (3):335-344.

Hayden, J. D. 1969. Gyratory crushers of the Sierra Pinacate, Sonora. American Antiquity 34 (2): 154-161.

Hayden, J. D. 1972. Hohokam petroglyphs of the Sierra Pinacate, Sonora, and the Hohokam shell expeditions. Kiva 37(2): 74-83.

Hayden, J. D. 1976. Pre-altithermal archaeology in the Sierra Pinacate, Sonora, Mexico. American Antiquity 41 (3):274-289.

Hayden, J. C. 1981 (unsigned). C-14 ages of foodshell from occupied dunes of the Bay of Adair, Sonora, Mexico.American Antiquity 46: 933.

Hayden, J. D. 1985. Food animal cremations of the Sierra Pinacate, Sonora, Mexico. Kiva 50 (4): 237-248.

Hayden, J. D. 1988. The Sierra del Pinacate, pp. 52-56. In: *Simposio de Investigación sobre la Zona Ecológica de El Pinacate*. Comité de Ecología y Medio Ambiente, Comisión Sonora-Arizona. Hermosillo, Sonora, México.

Hayden, J. D. 1998. *The Sierra Pinacate*. University of Arizona Press, Tucson.

Hayden, J. D., Nabhan, G. P., Broyles, B., Williams, A., and Wilson, C. 1993. Sheep cremations and massacres, pp. 27-36. In: *Counting Sheep* (Nabhan, G. P., ed.). University of Arizona Press, Tucson.

Heisey, A. 2000. *Under the Sun: A Sonoran Desert Odyssey*. Rio Nuevo Publishers, Tucson.

Henry, R. S. 2007. Mammals of the Sonoran Desert borderland reserves, pp. 272-279. In: *Dry Borders: Great Natural Reserves of the Sonoran Desert* (Felger, R. S., and Broyles, B., eds). University of Utah Press, Salt Lake City.

Hodgson, W. C. 2001. *Food Plants of the Sonoran Desert*. University of Arizona Press, Tucson.

Hornaday, W. T. 1983. *Camp-fires on Desert and Lava*. University of Arizona Press, Tucson (first published 1908, Charles Scribner's and Sons, New York).

Ivanyi, C. 2000. Fishes in the desert, pp. 509-526. In: *A Natural History of the Sonoran Desert* (Phillips, S. J., and Comus, P. W., eds.). Arizona-Sonora Desert Museum Press (Tucson) and University of California, Press, Berkeley.

Ives, R. L. 1942. The discovery of Pinacate Volcano. Scientific Monthly 54: 230-237.

Ives, R. L. 1960. The last journey of Melchior Díaz. Journal of Geography 49: 61-66.

Ives, R. L. 1962. In memorium—Alberto Celaya. Explorers Journal 40: 91-92.

Ives, R. L. 1963. The bell of San Marcelo. Kiva 29: 14.

Ives, R. L. 1964. The Pinacate region, Sonora, Mexico. Occasional Papers of the California Academy of Sciences 47: 1-43.

Ives, R. L. 1989. *Land of Lava, Ash and Sand: The Pinacate Region of Northwestern Mexico* (Byrkit, J. W., and Dahood, K. J., compilers). Arizona Historical Society, Tucson.

Jahns, R. H. 1959. Collapse depressions of the Pinacate Volcanic Field, Sonora, Mexico, pp. 165-184. In: *Southern Arizona Guidebook, II*. Arizona Geological Society, Tucson.

Kresan, P. L. 2007. A geologic tour of the dry borders region, pp. 31-45. In: *Dry Borders: Great Natural Reserves of the Sonoran Desert* (Felger, R. S., and Broyles, B., eds.). University of Utah Press, Salt Lake City.

Lancaster, N. 1989. The dynamics of star dunes: an example from the Gran Desierto, Mexico. Sedimentology 36: 273-289.

Lancaster, N., Greeley, R., and Christensen, P. R. 1987. Dunes of the Gran Desierto sand-sea, Sonora, Mexico. Earth Surface Processes and Landforms 12: 277-288.

Lumholtz, C. 1990. *New Trails in Mexico: An Account of One Year's Exploration in North-Western Sonora, Mexico and South-Western Arizona, 1909-1910.* University of Arizona Press, Tucson, Arizona (first published 1912, Charles Scribner's and Sons, New York, and later reprinted by Rio Grande Press).

Lutz, T. M. and Gutmann, J. T. 1995. An improved method for determining and characterizing alignments of pointlike features and its implications for the Pinacate volcanic field, Sonora, Mexico. Journal of Geophysical Research 100 (B9):17, 659-17, 670.

Lynch, D. J. 1981. Genesis and geochronology of alkaline volcanism in the Pinacate Volcanic Field, northwestern Sonora, Mexico. Ph.D. dissertation, Department of Geosciences, University of Arizona, Tucson.

Lynch, D. J. 1989. Neogene volcanism in Arizona: the recognizable volcanoes. In: *Geologic Evolution of Arizona* (Jenney, J. P., and Reynolds, S. J., eds.). Arizona Geological Society Digest 17: 681-700.

Lynch, D. J. 1991. Pinacate's largest lava flow. CEDO News (Puerto Peñasco) 4 (1): 1-3, 6-13.

Lynch, D. J., and Gutmann, J. T. 1987. Volcanic structures and alkaline rocks in the Pinacate Volcanic Field of Sonora, Mexico. Arizona Bureau of Geology and Mineral Technology Special Paper 5: 309-322.

Lynch, D. J., Musselman, T. E., Gutmann, J. T., and Patchett, P. J. 1993. Isotopic evidence for the origin of Cenozoic volcanic rocks in the Pinacate volcanic field, northwestern Mexico. Lithos 29: 295-302.

May, L. A. 1973. Resource reconnaissance of the Gran Desierto region, northwestern Sonora, Mexico. Master's thesis, Department of Watershed Management, University of Arizona, Tucson.

McAuliffe, J. R. 2000. Desert soils, pp. 87-104. In: *A Natural History of the Sonoran Desert* (Phillips, S. J., and Comus, P. W., eds.). Arizona-Sonora Desert Museum Press (Tucson) and University of California Press, Berkeley.

Minckley, W. L., Miller, R. R., and Norris, S. M. 2002. Three new pupfish species, *Cyprinodon* (Teleostei, Cyprinodontidae), from Chihuahua, México, and Arizona, USA. Copeia 2002 (3): 687-705.

Murrieta Saldivar, J. 2000. Scenic beauty and human perceptual dimensions of The Pinacate and Gran Desierto de Altar Biosphere Reserve, Sonora, Mexico (Visitors, Community and Managers). Ph.D. dissertation, University of Arizona, Tucson.

Nabhan, G. P. 1985. *Gathering the Desert.* University of Arizona Press, Tucson.

Nations, D., and Stump, E. 1996. *Geology of Arizona*. Kendall/Hunt Publishing Co., Dubuque, Iowa.

Pacheco, M., Martín-Barajas, A., Elders, W., Espinosa-Cardeña, J. M., Helenes, J., and Segura, A. 2006. Stratigraphy and structure of the Altar basin of NW Sonora: implications for the history of the Colorado River delta and the Salton trough. Revista Mexicana de Ciencias Geológicas 23 (1): 1-22.

Pfeifer, E., Beard, S., Bronk, J., Casebier, D., Gordon, L., Haxel, G., Hendricks, J., Kresan, P., Lowry, S., MacKinnon, D., Mullins, K., Petryszan, Y., Pierce, F., Priest, S., Roldan-Quitana, J., and Swann, G. 1992. Reference Material and Guidebook for: Geologic Field Trip to the Pinacate Region, Northwest Sonora and Organ Pipe Cactus National Monument, Southwest Arizona. United States Geological Survey, Flagstaff, Arizona. Third Annual Science Teacher's Workshop, December 3-6, 1992.

Pfeifer, E., Duffield, W., MacKinnon, D., Beard, S., Priest, S., Ruhlman, J., Haxel, G., Rosanova, T., Coleman, J., Hendricks, J., and Swann, G. 1997. Reference Material and Guidebook for: Geologic Field Trip to the Pinacate Volcanic Field, Northwest Sonora, MX. United States Geological Survey, Flagstaff, AZ. 8th Annual Science Teachers Workshop, December 2, 9, 11-14, 1997.

Phillips, S. J. and Comus, P. W. (eds.). *A Natural History of the Sonoran Desert*. Arizona-Sonora Desert Museum Press (Tucson) and University of California Press, Berkeley.

Schmidt, N. 1990. Plate tectonics and the Gulf of California region. Arizona Geology 20 (2): 1-4.

Secretaria de Medio Ambiente, Recursos Naturales y Pesca. 1995. Reserva de la Biósfera de El Pinacate y Gran Desierto de Altar. Programa de Manejo (2): Áreas Naturales Protegidas. Instituto Nacional de Ecologia, México, D. F.

Shackley, M. S. 1995. Sources of archaeological obsidian in the greater American Southwest: an update and quantitative analysis. American Antiquity 60 (3): 531-551.

Shackley, M. S. 2005. *Obsidian*. University of Arizona Press, Tucson.

Sheinbaum, J. 1998. What causes El Niño and how does it affect us? CEDO News (Puerto Peñasco) 8(2): 1, 6-9, 11-12.

Sheridan, T. E. 1996. Diet and diabetes among the O'odham. In: *Paths of Life: American Indians of the Southwest and Northern Mexico*. (Sheridan, T. E., and Parezo, N. J., eds). University of Arizona Press, Tucson.

Sykes, G. 1984. *A Westerly Trend*. Arizona Historical Society and University of Arizona Press, Tucson.

Taylor, R. E., Haynes, C. V., and Stuiver, M. 1996. Clovis and Folsom age estimates: stratigraphic context and radiocarbon calibration. Antiquity 70 (269): 505-525.

Turrin, B. D., Gutmann, J. T., and Swisher, C. C. III. 2008. A 13 ± 3 ka age determination of a tholeiite, Pinacate volcanic field, Mexico, and improved methods for 40Ar/39Ar dating of young basaltic rocks. Journal of Volcanology and Geothermal Research 177 (4): 848-856.

Urrea, L. A. 2004. *The Devil's Highway*. Little, Brown and Company, New York.

Van den Dolder, E. M. 1992. Rock varnish and rock pavement provide geological and archaeological records. Arizona Geology, Arizona Geological Survey 22 (1): 1, 4-7.

Van Devender, T. R. 2007. Ice Age in the Sonoran Desert: Pinyon pines and Joshua trees in the dry borders region, pp. 58-68. In: *Dry Borders: Great Natural Reserves of the Sonoran Desert* (Felger, R. S., and Broyles, B., eds.). University of Utah Press, Salt Lake City.

Van Devender, T. R., Burgess, T. L., Felger, R. S., and Turner, R. M. 1990. Holocene vegetation of the Hornaday Mountains of northwestern Sonora, Mexico. Proceedings of the San Diego Society of Natural History 2: 1-19.

Wilson, C. 2001. Reserva de la Biosfera del Pinacate. Waller Printing, Tucson, 1 p. brochure.

Waters, M. R. and Stafford, T. W. Jr. 2007. Redefining the Age of Clovis: Implications for the Peopling of the Americas. Science 315 (5815):1049.

Wood, C. A. 1972. Reconnaissance geology & geophysics of the Pinacate craters, Sonora, Mexico. Master's thesis, University of Arizona, Tucson.

Wood, C. A. 1974. Reconnaissance geophysics and geology of the Pinacate craters, Sonora, Mexico. Bulletin of Volcanology 38: 149-172.

ENDNOTES

1 Hartmann, 1989; Cochran et al., 1990, p. 2
2 Wilson, 2001
3 Ives, 1989
4 Hayden, 1998
5 Gutmann et al., 2000
6 Broyles et al., 2007, p. 644
7 Daniel Lopez, personal communication
8 Murrieta, 2000
9 Búrquez and Castillo, 1994, p. 12
10 Murrieta, 2000
11 Broyles et al., 2007, p. 662; Hartmann, 1989, p. 19
12 Felger et al., 1997, p. 414
13 Brusca and Bryner, 2004, p. 41
14 Lynch, 1981
15 Donnelly, 1974
16 Lynch, 1981, 1989; Wilson, 2001
17 Broyles et al., 2007, pp. 602, 645
18 Lancaster et al., 1987; Lancaster, 1989
19 Kresan, 2007; Beveridge et al., 2006
20 Brusca and Bryner, 2004, p. 10
21 Broyles et al., 2007, p. 664
22 Gutmann, 2002; following Jahns, 1959
23 Ezcurra et al., 1988
24 Peggy Boyer and José Campoy, personal communication
25 Fred Croxen, personal communication
26 Minckley et al., 2002; Echelle et al., 2005
27 Echelle et al., 2005
28 Anderson et al., 2005, p. 7
29 Nations and Stump, 1996, p. 175
30 J. T. Gutmann, personal communication
31 Kresan, 2007; Lynch, 1991
32 Lynch, 1991, pp. 1,2,6
33 Gutmann, 1976
34 Lynch and Gutmann, 1987
35 Gutmann, 2002
36 J. T. Gutmann, personal communication
37 Cochran et al., 1990, p. 4
38 May, 1973; Gutmann, 1976; Hartmann, 1989; Broyles et al., 2007
39 May, 1973
40 Wood, 1972
41 Hartmann, 1989, p. 144
42 Gutmann, 2002
43 Possibly by Jahns (1959) for his informant
44 Gutmann, 2002
45 Hartmann, 1989, p. 161
46 Gutmann, 2002
47 Lumholtz, 1912 (reprinted 1990)
48 Lynch, 1981, p. 63, Fig. 53
49 Gutmann, 1976
50 Gutmann, 2002
51 Damon et al., 1963
52 J. T. Gutmann, personal communication
53 Gutmann and Turrin, 2006
54 Lynch, 1981
55 Gutmann, 2002
56 Hornaday, 1908 (reprinted 1983)
57 Hornaday, 1908 (reprinted 1983)
58 Ives, 1964
59 Hartmann, 1989, p. 158
60 Hornaday, 1908 (reprinted 1983)
61 Broyles et al., 2007, p. 666
62 Lynch, 1981
63 Lynch, 1981
64 Lynch, 1981
65 Gutmann, 1976
66 Gutmann et al., 2000; Gutmann and Turrin, 2006
67 Gutmann, 2007, p. 236; Turrin et al., 2008
68 Gutmann and Turrin, 2006
69 Schmidt, 1990; http://pubs.usgs.gov/publications/text/Farallon.html
70 Lynch, 1989; Lynch et al., 1993
71 Kresan, 2007
72 Lutz and Gutmann, 1995
73 Felger et al., 1997, p. 414; Búrquez and Castillo, 1994, p. 20
74 Boyer, 2004
75 Secretaria de Medio Ambiente, Recursos Naturales y Pesca, 1995, p. 19
76 Ezcurra et al., 1988, p. 37; Búrquez and Castillo, 1994, p. 21
77 Kresan, 2007, p. 36
78 McAuliffe, 2000, p. 94
79 Hayden, 1998, pp. 24-25
80 McAuliffe, 2000, p. 97
81 McAuliffe, 2000, p. 99
82 Brusca and Bryner, 2004, p. 26
83 Davis et al., 1990a, p. 2
84 Van Devender, 2007; Van Devender et al., 1990
85 Van Devender et al., 1990; Van Devender, 2007
86 Felger, 2000, 2007b
87 Cochran et al., 1990, p. 9
88 Felger, 2007b
89 Dimmitt, 2000, p. 263
90 Wilson, 2001
91 Felger, 2007b
92 Felger, 1998, p. 1
93 Felger et al., 2007b
94 Felger et al., 2007b
95 R. Brusca, personal communication; provided invertebrate section; for additional details on invertebrates see articles in S. Phillips and P. Comus, 2000.
96 Búrquez and Castillo, 1994, pp. 9-63
97 Ivanyi, 2000, p. 525
98 Cochran et al., 1990, p. 5
99 Brusca and Bryner, 2004; Griffin, 2007 provides a checklist of birds recorded in the protected areas surrounding the Pinacate
100 May, 1973
101 May, 1973, p. 107
102 Cochran et al., 1990, p. 6
103 Búrquez and Castillo, 1994, p. 32
104 Henry, 2007, pp. 276-277
105 Broyles et al., 2007, p. 601
106 Urrea, 2004
107 Broyles et al., 2007, p. 678
108 Broyles et al., 2007, pp. 649-650
109 Broyles et al., 2007, p. 588; Granger, 1982
110 Taylor et al., 1996; Waters and Stafford, 2007, p. 1049
111 Hartmann, 1989, p. 129
112 Hayden, 1976, 1998
113 Hayden, 1981; Bowen, 1998
114 Jonathan Mabry, personal communication
115 Steve Hayden, personal communication
116 Jonathan Mabry, personal commnication
117 Hayden, 1967; Van Devender, 2007
118 Jonathan Mabry, personal communication
119 Hartmann, 1989, p. 131
120 Hayden, 1969
121 Wilson, 2001
122 Ferg and Peachey, 1998
123 Hayden, 1972
124 Ezell, 1955
125 Wilson, 2001; Hayden, 1985; Hayden et al., 1993
126 Jonathan Mabry, personal communication
127 Hodgson, 2001; Felger, 2007a
128 Felger, 2007a, p. 148
129 Wilson, 2001
130 Lumholtz, 1912, p. 286; Shackley, 1995, p. 533; Shackley, 2005, p. 79; http://www.swxrflob.net/losvidrios.htm
131 Hayden, 1988, p. 54
132 Wilson, 2001
133 Lumholtz, 1990, p. 333 (first published 1912); Hartmann, 1989, p. 141; Hayden, 1988, p. 54; Hayden, 1998, p. 33
134 Lumholtz, 1990, pp. 201-203 (first published 1912); Secretaria de Medio Ambiente, Recursos Naturales y Pesca, 1995, p. 46; Broyles et al., 2007, p. 645
135 May, 1973
136 Daniel Lopez, personal communication
137 Búrquez, 2001, p. 185
138 Lumholtz, 1990, pp. 201-203 (first published 1912, pp. 201-203)
139 Hartmann, 1989, p. 131
140 Brusca, 2004, p. 17
141 Ives, 1989, p.156-158, quoting ancient sources
142 Ives, 1960
143 Ives, 1989, p.158
144 Ives, 1989, p.18
145 www.catholicity.com/encyclopedia/; Brusca and Bryner, 2004, p. 10
146 Ives, 1989, p.18
147 Ives, 1942, p. 235
148 Sheridan, 1996, p.134
149 Hartmann, 1989
150 Ives, 1989
151 Juan María Salvatierra, in Ives, 1989, p.19
152 Juan Mateo Manje, in Hartmann, 1989, p. 50; this may have been MacDougal Crater (Ives, 1964, p. 22)
153 Hardy, 1977 (first published 1829)
154 Hartmann, 1989, p. 78
155 Lynch, 1981, pp. 20, 22
156 Audubon, 1984 (first published 1906)
157 Coffman, 1997; Dictionary of the English Language: Fourth Edition; http://www.bartleby.com/61/25/GO272500.html
158 Hartmann, 1989, p. 92 quoting Ives, 1963
159 Bill Broyles, personal communication
160 Hartmann, 1989, p. 96
161 Hornaday, 1983 (first published 1908)
162 Ives, 1989, p. 45
163 Sykes, 1984, p. 272
164 Hornaday, 1983 (first published 1908)
165 Lumholtz, 1990 (first published 1912)
166 Hornaday, 1983, p. 193
167 Phinney, W., no date: http://history.nasa.gov/alsj/ap-geotrips.pdf
168 M. Justin Wilkinson, personal communication
169 Murrieta, 2000; José Dávila Paulin, personal communication.; yet this website reports 67 ejidos in the Pinacate http://www.parksinperil.org/files/page_4_el_pinacate_biosphere_reserve.pdf
170 Wilson, 2001